STUDY GUIDE

TO ACCOMPANY

Bloom and Lazerson

Brain, Mind, and Behavior
SECOND EDITION

STUDY GUIDE

TO ACCOMPANY

Bloom and Lazerson

Brain, Mind, and Behavior

SECOND EDITION

TIMOTHY J. TEYLER, Ph.D.
Northeast Ohio College of Medicine

Assisted by:

Larry Cauller
Nick Chiaia
Pascal DiScenna
Linda Prior
Bennett Rosenthal
Ron Salafia
Geoff Yuen

An Annenberg/CPB Project

W. H. Freeman and Company
New York

Printed in the United States of America

ISBN 0-7167-1894-4

2 3 4 5 6 7 8 9 0 VB 6 5 4 3 2 1 0 8 9

CONTENTS

PREFACE

Welcome to an exciting adventure. This course on BRAIN, MIND, AND BEHAVIOR is an introduction to a fascinating world -- the world that exists inside the human brain.

As Jacob Bronowski said before his death, "All the best young scientists are now working on the brain." In the last quarter of a century, science has mounted an assault on the mysteries of the brain. Armed with new techniques from nuclear medicine, genetics, immunology and other fields researchers are breaking interdisciplinary barriers and finding fresh answers to central questions of our existence. If the 20th century is the Age of Science, surely the 1980's is the Decade of the Brain. In this course you will be a witness to the brains' surrender of some of its secrets.

The textbook for this course is _Brain, Mind, and Behavior, Second Edition_, authored by Floyd E. Bloom and Arlyne Lazerson, and published by W.H. Freeman and Company.

COURSE GOALS

This course was developed to provide you with the latest information in our understanding of the brain and its relation to behavior. No particular background in science is required or expected of you. Rather, this course is intended for students from a variety of backgrounds. Because of this, the authors of the textbook and of this *Study Guide* have included extensive discussions and descriptions of the material presented in the course.

It is our goal that by the end of this course you will be able to

1. Describe the elements of the brain and their circuits.

2. Describe the major functions of the brain and explain how they work.

3. Appreciate that all human behavior, thought and feelings are the end result of complex patterns of brain activity.

4. Appreciate how the neuroscientist goes about studying the brain.

5. Understand some of the major diseases and disorders of the brain and what is done to treat them.

6. Understand our theme for the course - the fundamental assumption that all the normal functions of the healthy brain and the disorders of the diseased brain, no matter how complex, can ultimately be explained in terms of the basic components of the brain and the ways in which they interact.

DEVELOPING GOOD STUDY HABITS

The development and practice of good study habits are essential to gaining the most from this course. Self-discipline with respect to the points discussed below will greatly assist you in becoming an effective learner in both this course and others.

Study Schedule

One of the most beneficial things that you can do to become a better learner is to set aside a regular time for study. It is tempting to let the course assignments slide and to cram right before examinations. You may even to able to get through the course by adopting this strategy. However, you will be cheating yourself because you will obtain much greater benefit from the textbook, the teacher and this study guide if you study regularly and keep up with the assignments.

While there are many ways to study effectively, all rely upon establishing a plan and sticking to it. One of the best plans is to prepare in advance for the class session by going through the first half of each chapter in the *Study Guide* and then reading the text chapter. By doing so you will be better able to appreciate the teacher's comments and be in a good position to ask meaningful questions and participate in class discussion. The second half of each chapter in this *Study Guide* is designed to be read after class and provides a review of the main points of the chapter; it also lists the important terms and test excercises.

Study Area

You cannot study effectively while watching television or listening to music. As elementary as this may seem, many students attempt to do so anyway. As you will learn in this course, the ability to focus attention is essential to engaging the higher centers of the brain. Therefore arrange to study in a setting where you will not be tempted to let your attention wander.

Many students find that studying in a library provides the right environment. If you choose to study at home or in your room, be sure to create an atmosphere conducive to focusing your attention on the course materials. A comfortable desk and chair, sufficient lighting, and freedom from visual and auditory distraction all contribute to good study habits.

Active Learning

You will learn best if you fully engage your brain processes in the task. Part of this can be accomplished by adhering to the suggestion above. In addition, if you can create situations in which you are an active participant in the learning process rather than a passive "sponge" or listener, so much the better. How can you be an active participant? One way is to use the material in the *Study Guide*. You will find questions to keep in mind as you study the chapters, self-test questions, and a place to try to outline the chapter after you read it. All of these study aids will help. In addition, as seasoned teachers know, one way to master a subject is to teach it. Therefore, if possible, form study groups in which you teach each other the chapter material. Often teachers frown upon students working together. Clearly, we are *not* suggesting that the prepared students do the work for the unprepared or lazy students. Rather, each student must be able to put the material of the chapter into his or her own terms. If you can explain something to a fellow student, you probably know it well yourself.

HOW TO USE THIS *STUDY GUIDE*

Each chapter in this *Study Guide* begins with a section that is to be read before reading the textbook chapter. The first part begins with a statement of the chapter <u>Objectives</u> and an <u>Outline</u>. The objectives should give you an idea of the major themes of the chapter and the areas that should be familiar to you when you are done. The outline lists the material to be covered in the chapter and shows how it is organized. The <u>Theme</u> tells you what will be encountered in the textbook chapter, emphasizing the main points. Included in the theme are examples, asides, and additional information related to the chapter content.   After you have read the chapter we recommend that you close the book and fill in the details of the major points of the chapter in the Student's Outline.   Then go back to the chapter, or your notes, and see how well you did in recalling these points.   In this way you will immediately see which parts of the chapter require more study.   The important terms used in the chapter are listed for you under Key Terms.   You should be sure that you are familiar with them.   The textbook Glossary provides their definition.

The *Study Guide* contains Self-Test items (and their answers) that you should use to see how well you have mastered the material in each chapter.

Brain, Mind, and Behavior, Second Edition and this Study Guide can be used in conjunction with the eight-part television series THE BRAIN produced by WNET in New York for the Public Broadcasting System. The programs of THE BRAIN telecourse convey the essence of modern brain research and its bearing on our knowledge of human behavior and complement the text and study guide.   The last section of this Study Guide is a Telecourse Guide to assist in linking the textbook material with that of the telecourse.   The textbook chapters associated with each telecourse program are provided and should be read prior to viewing the program.

Acknowledgments

The production of this course represents a team effort.   Floyd E. Bloom and Arlyne Lazerson wrote the textbook.   This *Study Guide* was written by Timothy J. Teyler with the assistance of Larry Cauller, Nick Chiaia, Pascal DiScenna, Linda Prior, Bennett Rosenthal, Ron Salafia and Geoff Yuen.   Editorial assistance was provided by Sharon Combs and Lou Stransky.

CHAPTER 1
INTRODUCTION TO THE NERVOUS SYSTEM

Before You Read This Chapter

OBJECTIVES

After reading this chapter you should be able to do the following:

1. Understand that the basic premise of this book is that both the normal functions of a healthy brain and the disorders of a diseased brain, no matter how complex, can ultimately be explained in terms of basic structural components of the brain.

2. Appreciate that the nervous system operates throughout the body and is responsible for our sensations and for our reactions to the world around us; it coordinates the functions of other organs and stores, organizes, and retrieves past experiences.

3. Be aware that the major activities of the brain are related to sensation, motion, internal regulation, reproduction, and adaptation.

4. Understand that the brain is subdivided into a large number of functional units that are specialized for the jobs they perform.

5. Be aware that by studying the structure and function of the brain, one can gain considerable insight into both human and animal behavior.

6. Be able to explain that the historical views of the brain, the mind, and human behavior were considerably influenced by the prevailing concepts of the times.

7. Know that the development of experimental and scientific methods by medical investigators and others led to the emergence of experiments that eventually contributed to our present conceptualization of the nervous system.

8. Understand that the scientific method consists of observation, interpretation and verification.

9. Appreciate that scientists work from observation to hypotheses, a process known as inductive reasoning. Or they may begin with global hypotheses and then formulate experiments to test them, a process known as deductive reasoning.

10. Appreciate that the nervous system has two main parts, the central
     nervous system and the peripheral nervous system. The central nervous
     system consists of the brain and the spinal cord, while the peripheral
     nervous system consists of the peripheral nerves and the autonomic
     and enteric nervous systems. The three major divisions of the
     brain are the forebrain, the midbrain, and the hindbrain.

OUTLINE

Why study the brain?

> Brain, mind, and behavior
> Brain and mind: A basic premise

What does the brain do?

> Sensation
> Motion
> Internal regulation
> Reproduction
> Adaptation

What is a brain?

Historical views of the brain, mind and behavior

> Analysis by analogy
> Analysis by observation and experimentation
> A contemporary analogy

The scientific method

The organization of the nervous system

The organization of the brain: An introduction

> The forebrain and its parts
> The telencephalon
> The diencephalon
> The midbrain and its parts
> The hindbrain and its parts

Two basic concepts of neuroscience

THEME

For many of you, the study of the nervous system and what it does may
come as a novel experience.   Traditionally, the study of the brain is
considered in biology courses, while the study of behavior, or what
the brain ultimately controls, is considered in psychology or
sociology courses.   In the last several decades, however, the field of
neuroscience has emerged as a separate and distinct discipline.   The

neuroscientist is concerned with both the brain's mechanism of operation, and the ultimate purpose of that operation--that is, behavior.

Is there a difference between the physical "stuff" of the brain--cells, neurotransmitters, and other biological phenomena--and the result of the operation of these biological material--that is, behavior? Clearly, there are differences in terms of the level of analysis and the level of description. One can describe the activities of nerve cells, as we shall do in these pages, and one can also describe the behavior of organisms, which we will also do. But what is the relationship between the two? Are they directly related? Is one the result of activity of the other? If so, how does one influence the other?

Mind and Behavior

One of the fundamental philosophical questions of the ages has been, what is the relation of the mind to the body? While in the minds of many this question is not resolved, the position we shall take in this book is that behavior is an emergent property of the operation of the brain.

The theme of this chapter, and the overall theme of the book, is that what we commonly refer to as the "mind" is really the end result of complicated interactions among countless nerve cells in various regions of the brain. Philosophically, people have taken two major positions over the centuries. One school of thought says that mind and body are two distinct and separate things and that one cannot understand the mind by understanding the details and operation of the body, which includes the brain. This position is known as dualism. The opposite position, called monism, maintains that the mind is an emergent property of the functioning of the body or, in this case, of the brain.

The position taken in this book is that of monism, which holds that all the properties of behavior and mind are ultimately explainable in terms of the operation of the biological organism. Some may object to the monistic approach because they feel that it denies the operation of free will and the possibility of a meaningful individual existence. While it is no doubt true that a monistic approach to behavior appears to reduce the richness and complexity of human behavior to relatively mechanical biological events, this is not the same as asserting that individuals have no control over their destinies.

As you will see as you progresses through the course, the degree of flexibility and of "creativity" that the mechanical brain is capable of attaining allows for an almost infinite degree of behavioral variations and therefore for the exercise of "free will. This is true because the machinery of the brain is exquisitely sensitive to the environment in which it lives. The brain changes it own structure and function as a result of its interactions with its surroundings. Therefore, your ability to make decisions, to act and have emotional responses is very much a product of the basic framework of the brain that you inherited from your parents, as well as of interactions with the environment in which you were raised and of which you continue to be a part.

We are not so presumptuous as to suggest that we have resolved an age-old philosophical dispute over mind and body. Rather, it is our intention to clearly state our position that scientific evidence can be marshaled to support the belief that mind and body are two aspects of the same phenomenon viewed from different perspectives.

What does the brain do?

Given the central importance of biological issues in behavior, one can ask the question: What exactly is it that the brain does? We see by looking at Table 1.1 in the text that the brain is involved in a wide spectrum of behaviors. It is instructive to reflect for a moment on how many of the activities in this table could be accomplished without calling into play some part of the brain. Clearly, single-celled animals are able to move about in their environment, yet they do not possess anything resembling a brain. Therefore, the possession of a brain by a more complicated, multi-cellular organism does not necessarily provide an entirely new spectrum of behaviors for its possessor but rather enables the organism to perform its necessary duties in a more effective and efficient manner. A single-celled organism, for example, may be at the mercy of its environment because it is unable to anticipate changes and cannot benefit from past experiences to control its interactions with the environment. As human beings, however, we have highly developed analytical abilities to help us solve a problem. These are the abilities of a very complicated brain indeed.

Sensation and Motion

It is traditional to think of the brain as being involved in five categories of activity--sensation, motion, internal regulation, reproduction, and adaptation. Through the use of our sensory apparatus we obtain raw data about the physical world in our immediate environment. Each of the sensory systems contains specialized transducers, called sensory receptors that convert physical energy in the form of light, pressure, and sound into neural impulses. Sir Charles Sherrington once stated that the function of the nervous system is to produce muscle contractions. Another way of saying this is that the ultimate expression of the brain is in movement--the second category of brain activity. While this statement may immediately rejected by some as incomplete because it appears not to provide a role for thinking and other covert actions, what Sherrington was referring to is that all such covert activities are for naught if they are never expressed in terms of movement. Voluntary and involuntary movements constitute the two main categories of motor behavior available to us.

Internal Regulation

A third major function of the brain is the regulation of internal bodily processes. Such essential functions as regulating body temperature, metabolism, digestion, and respiration are rarely given much thought because they occur automatically, but they are controlled rather precisely by specialized regions in the brain. The process of brain regulation of internal bodily activity, called homeostasis, is the subject of Chapter 5.

Reproduction

Maintenance of the species across generations is a powerful force in biology. It should come as no surprise, then, that the fourth brain function is to regulate reproductive activities. Reproductive behaviors are controlled by environmental cues interacting with internal physiological states, particularly in animals. Only in human beings do factors of experience and social influence play a significant role in mating and reproductive behaviors.

Adaptation

The fifth general category of brain activity, adaptation, refers to a wide range of brain responses to environmental situations. Adaptive responses include remembering how to solve a problem, learning how to cope with new situations, and molding the environment to help us cope better. Many of the behaviors considered to be most representative of human activity are examples of adaptive brain processes. The very fact that you are studying the brain at this point probably reflects an adaptive response that you have made to your environment, whether it is in preparation for a future career or in response to a deeply felt personal need. We can define the brain as a specialized organ designed to help individual organisms to carry out major acts of living.

Historical Views of Brain

The brain was not always thought to control behavior. Aristotle, for example, spoke of nervous control, not of the brain. It is important to realize, as stated in the text, that scientific thought is power-fully influenced by the "spirit of the times." It is commonplace today to draw parallels between the operation of the brain and familiar objects known to most of us (e.g., computers). Early thinkers studying brain function also referred to common objects in their environment. Galen drew parallels between the aqueducts of ancient Greece and the humors that he believed flowed through the body and controlled our behavior. These early ideas gradually gave way to our modern conceptualizations of the nervous system, mainly due to the growth of scientific thought. Early scientists began to perform experiments designed to test whether or not certain ideas about nature were correct. Galvani, for example, showed that nerves and muscles actually worked by generating electricity. The development of the scientific method, to be discussed shortly, was an important milestone in the history of scientific thought regarding brain structure and function.

By the early 19th century scientific thought had progressed to the point where two major approaches to the study of the brain were apparent. The first was the lesion approach, in which scientists took advantage of natural accidents or illness resulting in the destruc-tion of certan brain areas to study the results and changes in an organism's behavior. The other major method emerging at this time involved the deliberate electrical stimulation of regions of the brain and concomitant observations of the results. Over the years, based on experiments, the view gradually emerged that the brain was a complex collection of interacting individual cells that resulted in behavior.

Analogy as an Aid to Understanding Brain

Earlier we spoke of the analogy that Galen used between Greek aqueducts and vital humors. It's important to recognize that such analogies to common experience are still utilized today when trying to understand the structure and function of the brain. In the days when the telephone system was the most sophisticated instrument known to us, it was frequently written that the brain was like a complicated telephone switching network. Later, of course, analogies and parallels were drawn between the brain and the computer, the brain and holograms and, currently, the brain and parallel processing computers. As stated in the text, however, the goal is not to find a man-made parallel to the brain but rather to understand the nature of brain functions. It may be that the structure and function of the brain bear's little or no relationship to any man-made device.

The Scientific Method

The scientific method has been largely responsible for much of the progress made in understanding all aspects of nature, including brain structure and function. The scientific method rests upon these basic principles: (1) observation, (2) interpretation, and (3) verification. When a scientist begins by observing the behavior of the organism, collecting the facts, interpreting what this might mean, and verifying that the observations were accurate, the scientist is acting according to what is known as the method of inductive reasoning. The opposite approach is be begin with an idea or hypothesis regarding how a system works and then try to work back and obtain data that confirm or reject this hypothesis. In real life, scientists actually use some of both approaches when trying to ferret out the secrets of nature. While most scientists conduct their experiments using primarily inductive reasoning, many also utilize hunches and guesses to guide their inductive experiments.

The Organization of the Brain

It is possible to divide the brain into three major areas: the forebrain, the midbrain, and the hindbrain. The structures of the forebrain include the regions of the cortex and the thalamus and are responsible for the higher cognitive functions of behavior. The tiny midbrain consists of structures which are largely concerned with aspects of sensory behavior. The hindbrain consists of the cerebellum as well as numerous other structures and is concerned with homeostatic function, motor behavior, the relaying of sensory information, and other reflex-like adaptive responses.

The divisions of forebrain, midbrain, and hindbrain are based primarily on developmental and anatomical criteria. A different way of considering the brain is to look at the functional systems concerned with vision, motor behavior, emotionality, and the like.

The functional systems usually involve components from the forebrain, the midbrain, and the hindbrain organized in complex ways to perform the job at hand. In the course of studying this book, you will read about many of these functional systems of the brain and how they are organized and thought to operate. In this chapter we introduce a number of brain regions. While the names of these areas, such as the hippocampus and the thalamus, may not mean a great deal to you at this point, they will soon become familiar. You should attempt to gain a general understanding of the organization of the brain at this point. Detailed information about individual structures within the brain will come later on.

Throughout this book you will encounter the basic premise that both the normal functions of the healthy brain and the disorders of the diseased brain, no matter how complex, can ultimately be explained in terms of the basic structural components of the brain. Within this basic premise are two central concepts of neuroscience. (1) The nervous system operates throughout the body and is responsible for (a) sensing and reacting to the world around us, (b) coordinating the functions of other organs so the body can survive, and (c) storing, organizing, and retrieving past experiences. The nervous system does this through the central nervous system (composed of the brain and spinal cord) and the peripheral nervous system (consisting of the peripheral nerves, the autonomic nervous system--which regulates the activity of the internal organs--and the diffuse enteric nervous system--which regulates the digestive tract). (2) The separate functions of the nervous system are carried out by subsystems organized according to area of responsibility. Each of the brain's functions is the province of a separate system.

In the succeeding chapters of this book you will encounter the basic structure of the brain outlined in this chapter again and again. We will examine the kinds of activities that the brain controls--such things as sensation, movement, homeostasis, feelings, learning and memory, and thinking and consciousness--in the context of the structure and function of the components of the brain outlined in this chapter and presented in more detail in Chapter 2.

QUESTIONS TO KEEP IN MIND AS YOU READ THIS CHAPTER

1. What is the purpose of studying the structure, function, and mechanisms of the brain?

2. What can be revealed about the behavior of human beings from the study of the brain?

3. Does the position taken in this book violate the concept of free will?

4. Think of the jobs listed in Table 1.1. Can you imagine how it would be to be deprived of one more of them in a variety of daily activities?

5. Based on what you know about the historical use of analysis by analogy, reflect on current comparisons between computers or holograms and the brain.

6. There are a least 50 billion neurons in the human brain, all of which are connected in meaningful ways to other neurons. Do you think that science will ever understand this incredibly complex organ?

7. Think of examples of inductive and deductive reasoning you have utilized in your life.

8. Try to imagine the forces influencing such thinkers as Aristotle and Galen when they first confronted the mysteries of the mind.

9. How can it be that the brain processes information that is physically not present? Consider a dream or an illusion.

10. Some drugs have the ability to alter thought processes. How do you suppose these drugs are able to influence the way the brain functions?

After You Have Read The Chapter, Continue With The Following Material

STUDENT'S OUTLINE

After you have read this chapter and studied the material it contains, close the book and in the space below, using your own words, try to outline the major points that you have just read. The basic structure of the chapter is provided below.

Why study the brain?

What does the brain do?

What is a brain?

Historical views of the brain, mind, and behavior

The scientific method

The organization of the nervous system

The organization of the brain: An introduction

Two basic concepts of neuroscience

Now that you have attempted to outline this chapter from memory, go back to the textbook and see how accurate your recollection was. Fill in those topics you might have missed and emphasize the points that are stressed in the textbook.

Key Terms

The following terms are introduced in this chapter (the terms are defined in the textbook). Be sure that you know these terms and can define them.

Audition
Autonomic nervous system
Basal ganglia
Brainstem
CAT scan
Central nervous system
Cerebellum
Cerebral cortex
Diencephalon
Diffuse enteric nervous system
Forebrain
Frontal lobe
Gustation
Hindbrain
Hippocampus
Limbic system
Medulla oblongata
Midbrain

Occipital lobe
Olfaction
Parietal lobe
Peripheral nervous system
Pons
Septum
Somatic sensation
Sulci
Telencephalon
Temporal lobe
Thalamus
Vestibular apparatus
Vision

SELF-TEST

Multiple Choice

1. The major categories of activities attributed to the brain are
   a. motion, reproduction, learning, sensation, and internal regulation
   b. behavior, reflexes, reproduction, motion, and sensation
   c. reproduction, internal regulation, adaptation, motion, and sensation
   d. learning, internal regulation, motion, and sensation

2. The major means by which the brain senses the world around it are
   a. audition, gustation, somatic sensation, and vision
   b. vision, vestibular sensation, gustation, somatic sensation, and audition
   c. audition, visceral sensation, gustation, somatic sensation, and olfaction
   d. olfaction, visceral sensation, hearing, and vision

3. Which of the following tools of research was shown by Camillo Golgi and Ramon y Cajal to be of critical importance to neuroscience?
   a. lesion studies
   b. electrical stimulation studies
   c. microscopic studies of chemically stained tissues
   d. none of the above

4. Which of the following is NOT a component of the scientific method?
   a. a hypothesis
   b. observation
   c. interpretation
   d. none of the above

5. Each neuron in the brain communicates, on average with _____ other neurons.
   a. 100
   b. 1,000
   c. 10,000
   d. 100,000

6. The early hypothesis about brain function that considered nerves to be hollow tubes through which gasses flowed to excite the muscles is called:
   a. the axonal flow theory
   b. the bile theory
   c. the balloonist theory
   d. the vital fluid theory

11

7. In the 1790's a new brain theory emerged which asserted that specialization's in brain faculties (such as combativeness, secretiveness) could be detected by palpating the location of bumps on the head. This theory is termed
    a. empirical behaviorism
    b. hemispheric specialization
    c. phrenology
    d. reflexology

8. The central nervous system (CNS) is composed of
    a. the brain and spinal cord
    b. all the nerves of the body
    c. brain, spinal cord, autonomic nervous system
    d. the brain

9. Which of the following represents a correct sequence from a major division of the brain to an appropriate subdivision and specific brain area?
    a. midbrain, telencephalon, brainstem
    b. forebrain, diencephalon, thalamus
    c. hindbrain, medulla, basal ganglia
    d. forebrain, hippocampus, septum

10. Which of the following pairs of cortical lobes and their function are correct?
    a. occipital lobe, movement
    b. frontal lobe, body senses
    c. parietal lobe, hearing
    d. temporal lobe, hearing

11. The division of the nervous system primarily responsible for regulating the internal environment of the brain (heart, lungs, blood vessels, etc.) is the
    a. autonomic nervous system
    b. central nervous system
    c. diffuse enteric nervous system
    d. peripheral nervous system

12. The hypothesis issued by the newly formed Royal Society of England to explain nervous activation of muscle was
    a. the balloonist theory
    b. the vital fluid theory
    c. the gas theory
    d. none of the above

13. What English anatomist discovered a chemical method for detecting strands of dying nerves?
    a. Camillo Golgi
    b. Otto Loewi
    c. Sir Henry Dale
    d. Augustus Von Waller

14. Lesion and stimulation experiments showed that animals would die when these structures were destroyed:
    a. the basal ganglia
    b. the outer layers of the brain
    c. deep structures of the midbrain
    (d.) deep structures of the hindbrain

15. What scientist proposed that brain activity was transmitted by a vibrating ethereal medium?
    a. Isaac Newton
    b. Galen
    c. Johannes Kepler
    d. Thomas Willis

True or False

F 1. *Aristotle*
   Heraclitus wrote that the heart was both the seat of the soul and the center of nervous control.

F 2. *Autonomic*
   The peripheral nervous system is responsible for regulating such internal functions as digestion and respiration.

F 3. Psychology is the study of an organism's behavioral responses to both its internal and external environments. *not*

T 4. Neurons and glia are the two main classes of cells in the central nervous system.

F 5. *Frontal lobe*
   The cerebellum is that part of the forebrain that is involved in motor coordination. *Hindbrain*

T 6. The function of the occipital lobe of the cerebral cortex is to process visual information.

F 7. Historically, studies of the mind have focused upon the physical brain.

T 8. The vestibular apparatus, located within the skull beneath the ear, allows us to orient our bodies in space.

F 9. Goosebumps are caused by the voluntary movement of muscles found under the skin. *Autonomic—involuntary*

F 10. Hearing occurs when special receptors of the retina are activated by sound. *osicles in cochlea*

T 11. Lesion studies were useful in defining large areas of the brain in terms of their behavioral function.

T 12. One scientist who helped to establish the chemical transmission hypothesis of neuronal interaction was Otto Loewi. *Dale*

T 13.   The pons is located in the hindbrain.

T 14.   Magnetic resonance imaging allows a detailed view of the interior of the human brain.

F 15.   The cerebral hemispheres, hippocampus and amygdala are all part of the diencephalon. *Telencephalon*

Matching

A.   *Match the following individuals with their major contributions to the neurosciences.*

C	Galen	a.	chemical transmission hypothesis
d	Kepler	b.	staining technique for visualizing cells
f	Willis	c.	lesion and stimulation technique
g	Du Bois-Reymond	d.	optical properties of the eye
b	Cajal	e.	dissection of human and animal brains
a	Dale	f.	receptors in cochlea responsible for hearing
		g.	brain function explained on physical and chemical basis

B.   *Match the following functions to the structures that are responsible for them.*

d	vision	a.	pituitary
c	reflexes	b.	hypothalamic nuclei
g	sleep	c.	spinal motor neurons
f	complex joint movement	d.	receptors, relay nuclei, and cortical maps
e	initiation and movement patterns	e.	cerebellum, basal ganglia
		f.	cortex and thalamus
		g.	brainstem

Short Answer

1.   Describe the basic structure of the human brain.

2.   Discuss the history of ideas about brain function.

3.   What are the two basic concepts that guide research aimed at understanding the nervous system?

4.   What is the mind-brain problem?

5.   The body utilizes two types of movement--voluntary and involuntary. Define these and give examples of each.

ANSWERS TO SELF-TEST

Multiple Choice

1. c	2. a	3. c	4. d	5. c	6. c	7. c
8. a	9. b	10. d	11. a	12. b	13. d	14. d
15. a						

True and False

1. F	2. F	3. F	4. T	5. F	6. T	7. F
8. T	9. F	10. F	11. T	12. T	13. T	14. T
15. F						

Matching

A.		B.	
	e		d
	d		c
	f		g
	g		f
	b		e
	a		

CHAPTER 2
THE CELLULAR MACHINERY OF THE BRAIN

Before You Read This Chapter

OBJECTIVES

After reading this chapter, you should be able to do the following:

1. Be able to explain that all brain activity is a result of interactions between the elements of the brain--the neurons, the glia, and the various chemicals that are important in brain function.

2. Appreciate that nerve cells communicate with one another in a number of ways.

3. Understand that the function of neurotransmitters that are released from neurons is to influence the activity of other neurons.

4. Appreciate that the nervous system operates together with all the organs in the body to maintain appropriate internal conditions in light of changing external conditions.

5. Be able to explain how neuronal excitation comes about as a result of the movement of ions across the neuronal membrane.

6. Understand how the chemical messages sent by the neurotransmitters act on ion channels in the postsynaptic neuronal membrane.

7. Know that the function of these channel openings, in the simplest sense, is to cause the recipient neuron to become more or less excitable.

8. Appreciate that specialized jobs are performed by different aspects of the neuron--the dendrites, the soma and the axon.

9. Understand that synaptic communication between nerve cells is quite specific and is also capable of being modified.

10. Know that non-neuronal cells have particular roles and contribute to brain functioning--in particular, the glial cells and the cells that make up the blood-brain barrier--and help to produce the cerebrospinal fluid.

OUTLINE

Neurons

What neurons have in common with other cells
    Plasma membrane
    Cytoplasm and organelles
    Nucleus
Unique features of neurons
    Axons and dendrites
    Neuronal organelles
Labeling of neurons

Regulation of neuronal activity

The neuron at rest
The nerve impulse
Inhibition of nerve impulses

How neurons communicate

What happens at synapses
To fire or not to fire
Conditional messages
Modifiability of neuronal function

Synaptic transmitters

Amino acid transmitters
Monoamine transmitters
    Acetylcholine
    Dopamine, norepinephrine, and epinephrine
    Serotonin
Peptides

Patterns of neuronal circuitry

Hierarchical circuits
Local-circuit neurons
Single-source/divergent circuits

Other cells and structures of the nervous system

Glia
Vascular elements
Connective tissue elements

17

THEME

The title of this chapter summarizes a major theme of this chapter and the entire book: the brain is a very complicated biological machine. Its function is to process information about things in the environment. The machinery of the brain enables us to understand the meaning of sensory experiences by placing them into the context our previous experience. Thus, we can produce a behavioral response that is appropriate to the sensory experience. In addition, the information-processing capability of the brain provides us with emotional responses, our motivation to perform certain acts, and the operation of our bodily organs.

Neurons

The machinery that makes all this possible is composed of billions upon billions of individual neurons. In this chapter, we examine some of the properties of neurons and begin to see ways in which they interact with one another. Neurons can only function by interacting, and it is their interaction in your brain that makes possible the understanding of the words that you are reading at this moment. Reflect for a moment upon what must be going on inside your brain as you read, understand, and reflect upon these words. First, your eyes are scanning the page, sending messages to your brain regarding patterns of lines and angles and contours. Sensory regions in your brain must then decode these geometric forms and interpret them as language that has a meaning to you in relation to your previous experience. This is a very complicated example of brain processing, which calls upon the highest centers in the cortex for proper operation. If, however, the words on this page were printed in Italian, most of the readers of this study guide probably would not be able to understand them. Surely, the kinds of elementary visual sensations you receive are rather similar for both Italian and English, for the same letters of the alphabet are used. However, the unique combinations of letters that are employed in the Italian language have no basis in your previous experience, and therefore they are meaningless to you.

A major goal of this chapter is to provide you with some principles of brain functioning. If you come from a nonbiological or a nonscientific background, these principles may initially seem irrelevant to the richness and diversity of human behavior. We shall attempt to show you how the basic principles of nervous system operation that are seen at the level of single neurons and in the transactions between groups of neurons can eventually lead to an understanding of complex human behavior. The very complicated interplay of billions of neurons secreting neurotransmitters at untold numbers of synaptic junctions in the brain makes these behaviors possible.

Regulation of neuronal activity

Neurons of the brain are like other cells of the body in many respects. They possess a limiting membrane, a nucleus, mitochondria, and protein synthetic machinery. Where they differ, however, is in their ability to generate electrical activity and to transmit infor-

18

mation to other nerve cells. The electrical potential that is generated and travels down the lengthy axon is termed an action potential. When the action potential reaches the end of the axon, it triggers the release of neurotransmitter, which then floods into the minute synaptic gap separating the sending and the receiving neuron. The receiving neuron possesses receptor proteins that are capable of binding to the neurotransmitter and setting off activity in the receiving cell. The kind of activity that is generated is a function of the neurotransmitter. There are two major classes of neurotransmitters: excitatory and inhibitory. An excitatory neurotransmitter has actions at certain ion channels in the membrane of the receiving cell, causing the electrical potential of that cell to become less negative relative to the outside (that is, depolarized). If the recipient cell is sufficiently depolarized, it, in turn, will issue an action potential. The other type of neurotransmitter acts to open other ion channels in the membrane, causing the electrical potential of the cell to become more negative. The receiving cell is literally covered with hundreds of thousands of synaptic inputs, some of which are excitatory and some of which are inhibitory. It is the job of the receiving cell (its summating or integrative activity) to add up these excitatory and inhibitory influences and, if excitation exceeds inhibition by a critical amount, produce an action potential.

Synaptic transmission

Given the already complex nature of these interactions, it may come as a surprise that there may be as many as 20 different neurotransmitters. Some of these, such as glutamate and aspartate, are classified as excitatory and some as inhibitory, such as glycine and GABA. There are other neurotransmitters that can be either, depending upon the nature of the recipient cells. Part of the reason why there are so many different neurotransmitters is that there are chemical circuits within the brain that serve particular functions. A brain system containing norepinephrine originates in the locus coeruleus to synapse widely throughout the brain--and primarily controls arousal. This neurotransmitter system is distinct from one containing dopamine which originates in the ventral tegmentum and substantia nigra to supply motor areas of the brain, among other targets. The dopamine system, when dysfunctional, can result in Parkinson's disease (insufficient dopamine) or emotional disorders (excess dopamine). All neurotransmitters act by activating receptors on the postsynaptic membrane (and also autoreceptors on the presynaptic membrane). It is this aspect of synaptic transmission that pharmaceuticals exploit--acting on specific receptors to block or mimic the action of the neurotransmitter.

Neuronal Circuits

There are two things to note about the shape (what we call morphology) of neurons: (1) their dendritic trees, which are usually finely branched and are the sites of numerous synaptic contacts, sometimes onto small protrusions from the dendrite known as dendritic spines, and (2) the often lengthy axon from which neurotransmitter is released from its storage site in the vesicles of the axon terminals. Neurons come in a variety of shapes and sizes and their morphological appearance is a reliable clue to their location in the brain and presumably has some relation to their function. Neurons do not exist alone--they are almost always part of a circuit of some sort. The text describes three varieties of circuits that are commonly found in various portions of the brain: hierarchical circuits, local circuits, and single-source/divergent circuits.

1) Hierarchical circuits feature an organization whereby information flows into the nervous system through a chain of cells starting from sensory receptors, to secondary relays, to tertiary relays, and so forth.

2) Local circuits in the brain are generally composed of neurons whose function is to regulate the activity of other nearby neurons. In most cases, these local circuit neurons serve a negative feedback function. That is, their main job is to "turn off" the neighboring neuron once that neuron has issued an action potential.

3) The single-source/divergent circuit, is found in places in which one sending cell has many recipients (divergence).

All of these circuits, and others, work together in a highly complex fashion in the human brain. With billions of neurons and up to 10,000 synaptic contacts to and from each neuron, the wiring diagram of the human brain is not yet known. A further complicating factor in understanding the specificity of connections within the brain is that there is evidence accumulating that the brain is capable of "rewiring" itself. Experiments have shown a remarkable degree of "plasticity" or modifiability in which the structure and function of the nervous system changes in accordance with changing environmental conditions.

Other Cells and Structures

Neurons are not the only cells within the brain. Glial cells far outnumber neurons. However, efforts to discern their precise function have not always been unsuccessful. The text discusses three types of glial cells--astrocytes, oligodendrocytes, and Schwann cells. It is known that some glial cells (the astrocytes, for example) are involved in structural and metabolic support for neurons. Others form specialized structures, for example, the myelin covering of axons--a function of the oligodendrocytes and Schwann cells. Astrocyte glial cells perform a number of "clean-up" jobs, such as ridding the extracellular spaces of excess transmitters and ions. Unlike nerve cells, glial cells are not excitable.

Another major non-neural component of the brain is the vascular system, part of which comprises the blood-brain barrier. This barrier is actually a series of diffusional barriers that serve to prevent access of certain molecules to the brain. The blood-brain barrier is thus a protective mechanism to shield the brain from many of the chemicals that find their way into the blood stream. The blood-brain-barrier poses a serious problem to physicians who wish to get medications with demonstrated therapeutic benefit into the brain.

This chapter has focused on the neuron and its function. You have learned that neurons possess dendrites, upon which are located synapses to receive neuronal information from other cells in the brain. The synaptic connections between neurons employ neurotransmitters, chemicals that can serve either to excite or to inhibit the recipient cell. Neurotransmitters themselves are synthesized within the neuron from chemical material ultimately supplied by the food we eat. Neuronal excitability is a function of ion movements across membranes. Neurotransmitters affect recipient neurons by opening channels in the membrane to allow specific ions to flow across the neuronal membrane, thus giving rise to excitatory or inhibitory influences on that neuron. Although the synaptic connections between neurons are quite specific and not random, they are also modifiable and can change as a function of growth and development and of interactions with other neurons and their environment. Other cells in the brain are important for brain operations, including the glial cells and the cells that make up the blood-brain-barrier and produce the cerebrospinal fluid that bathes the brain. An important function of many neurons in the brain is to regulate the internal activities of organs of the body. This process, termed homeostasis, is the subject of Chapter 5.

In the chapters that follow, you will encounter many of the principles discussed in this chapter. We urge you to fully master the material presented here, as it will be referred to over and over again.

QUESTIONS TO KEEP IN MIND AS YOU READ THIS CHAPTER

1. What is the basic building block of the brain?

2. Explain how some neurotransmitters can be excitatory in their effect on the receiving cell while others are inhibitory.

3. Can you think of any behaviors or thoughts that are not the function of brain processes?

4. Why do you imagine there are so many neurons in the brain?

5. Do you think that the brains of animals such as dogs, cats and frogs are fundamentally different from your own brain?

6. Consider how the brain can process information that is physically not present, such as a dream or an illusion.

7. Some drugs have the ability to alter thought processes. How do you suppose these drugs are able to influence the way the brain functions?

STUDENT'S OUTLINE

After you have read this chapter and studied the material that it contains, close the book and in the space below, using your own words, try to outline the major points of what you have just read.

Neurons

Regulation of neuronal activity

How neurons communicate

Synaptic transmitters

Patterns of neuronal circuitry

Other cells and structure of the nervous system

Now that you have attempted to outline this chapter from memory, go back to the textbook and see how accurate your recollection was. Fill in those topics that you might have missed and emphasize the points that are stressed in the textbook.

Key Terms

The following terms were introduced in this chapter. Be sure that you know these terms and can define them.

Acetylcholine
Action potential
Amino acid transmitters
Astrocyte
Autoreceptor
Axon
Blood-brain-barrier
Catecholamines
Cerebrospinal fluid

Cholecystokinin
Choroid plexus
Convergent circuit
Cytoplasm
Cytoplasmic organelles
Dendrite
Depolarization
Divergent circuit
Dopamine
Endoplasmic reticulum
Endorphins
Epinephrine
Excitation
GABA
Glia
Golgi apparatus
Hierarchical circuit
Inhibition
Intracellular
Ions
Local circuit
Locus coeruleus
Meninges
Microtubules
Mitochondria
Monoamine oxidase
Myelin
Neuron
Neurotransmitter
Norepinephrine
Nucleus
Oligodendrocyte
Organelles
Peptides
Plasma membrane
Postsynaptic neuron
Presynaptic neuron
Resting potential
Reuptake
Ribosomes
Schwann cell
Serotonin
Smooth endoplasmic reticulum
Soma
Substance P
Substantia nigra
Summation
Synapse
Synaptic gap
Synaptic transmission (or neurotransmission)
Synaptic vesicles

Multiple Choice

1. The field of science concerned with the nervous system and brain is referred to as
   a. pathology
   b. cardiology
   c. neuroscience
   d. philosophy

2. Which of the following is true of the serotonin synapse
   a. site of action of the hallucinogenic drug LSD
   b. found at the nerve-muscle junction
   c. the first synapse to be identified
   d. Curare produces paralysis by acting here

3. Individual nerve cells are called
   a. glial cells
   b. neurons
   c. synapses
   d. ribosomes

4. The point at which two nerve cells are linked and communicate is called the
   a. neurotransmitters
   b. organelle
   c. synapse
   d. apparatus

5. Neurons communicate via chemical messengers called
   a. neurotransmitters
   b. synapses
   c. somata
   d. dendrites

6. The membrane that surrounds and encloses a nerve cell is called
   a. nuclear membrane
   b. plasma membrane
   c. cytoplasm
   d. endoplasm

7. The energy converters of nerve cells are the
   a. mitchondria
   b. microtubules
   c. ribosomes
   d. Golgi apparatus

8. The genetic information of the neuron is contained within the
   a. cytoplasm
   b. ribosomes
   c. mitochondria
   d. nucleus DNA

9. A neuron sends information to its recipient cells via the
   a. dendrite
   b. cell body
   c. soma
   d. axon

10. Axons do not contain
   a. cytoplasm
   b. synaptic vesicles
   c. neurotransmitters
   d. rough endoplasmic reticulum

11. Neurons that monitor internal or external events are called
   a. glial cells
   b. motor neurons
   c. sensory neurons
   d. relay neurons

12. Neurons that cause muscles to contract are called
   a. glial cells
   b. motor neurons
   c. sensory neurons
   d. relay neurons

13. When not firing an action potential, the electrical potential inside of a neuron (relative to the outside) is
   a. negatively charged
   b. positively charged
   c. neutral
   d. grounded

14. The following cells cannot divide after maturation
   a. glial cells
   b. astrocytes
   c. dendrites
   d. neurons

15. The specialized support cells of the nervous system are termed
   a. glia
   b. neurons
   c. choroid plexus
   d. axons

True or False

_T_ 1. The basic operating elements of the nervous system are neurons.

_F_ 2. Neurons have nothing in common with other cells of the body. *only diff = axons & dendrites*

_T_ 3. The passage of ions into the cell is regulated by channels in the plasma membrane.

_T_ 4. Synaptic transmitters alter the membrane properties of neurons.

_F_ 5. Biological functions of neurons cannot be modified.

_T_ 6. Wiring patterns of the brain are genetically specified.

_T_ 7. Genetically specified patterns of the brain can be modified locally by activity.

_F_ 8. The nervous system contains only nerve cells.

_T_ 9. Mature neurons are unable to divide.

_T_ 10. All of the muscles of the body, when fully active, draw about 25 percent more oxygen than the brain.

_F_ 11. Peptides are exclusively found in neurons.

_T_ 12. An individual neuron that synapses with many other neurons down the line is said to have divergent connections.

_T_ 13. The receiving surface of the neuron includes the dendrites.

_F_ 14. At synapses, information is transmitted in both directions. *only one* *axon - enter in*

_T_ 15. The nerve cell membrane contains channels that can be opened or closed by electrochemical messages.

Matching

_A_ 1. autoreceptors   A. feedback controlling transmitter synthesis

_B_ 2. dopamine   B. regulating emotional responses

_D_ 3. cytoplasm

_C_ 4. microtubules   C. holds the shape of axons and dendrites

_E_ 5. vesicles   D. all material enclosed by the plasma membrane

_H_ 6. soma

26

F 7. extracellular fluid

B 8. action potential

J 9. excitation

I 10. inhibition

E. contain neurotransmitters

F. high in sodium

G. depolarization of neuron

H. contains the nucleus

I. prevents cell from firing

J. stimulation of neuron to bring about depolarization

Short Answer

1. Diagram a hierarchial circuit.

2. What is the action potential?

3. Distinguish between excitation and inhibition of nerve cells.

4. What are three patterns of neuronal circuitry?

5. What is the blood-brain barrier?

ANSWERS TO SELF-TEST

Multiple Choice

1. c   2. a   3. b   4. c   5. a   6. b   7. a

8. d   9. d   10. d   11. c   12. b   13. a   14. d

15. a

True or False

1. T	2. F	3. T	4. T	5. F	6. T	7. T
8. F	9. T	10. T	11. F	12. T	13. T	14. F
15. T						

Matching

1. A
2. B
3. D
4. C
5. E
6. H
7. F
8. G
9. J
10. I

CHAPTER 3
LIFE-SPAN DEVELOPMENT OF THE BRAIN

Before You Read This Chapter

OBJECTIVES

After reading this chapter, you should be able to do the following:

1. Explain that the development of the nervous system from a primitive neural plate to the neural crest, the telencephalon, and the diencephalon provides a powerful framework for understanding interactions among regions of the brain.

2. Know that the development of the brain can be followed through eight major stages.

3. Understand that the development of the nervous system depends upon a rich interaction between genetic endowment and experience.

4. Be aware that the postnatal development of the brain consists almost entirely of the development of connections between nerve cells.

5. Understand that during the aging process, the central nervous system loses neurons and connections, yet compensates for them by continuing to form new synapses.

6. Appreciate that the aging human displays no deterioration in cognitive abilities--only displaying a decline in speed-related activities.

7. Understand that the sexual development of the brain and the organisms subsequent behavior depends upon the interaction of X and Y chromosomes with the hormonal environment and behavioral experience of the organism.

8. Appreciate that male/female differences in brain structure have been found in several regions of the central nervous system.

9. Know that a variety of trophic factors serve to guide and sculpt the nervous system during development.

10. Be able to explain that the phenomenon of cell death is a developmental pruning of excess cells based upon failed competition to achieve their targets.

OUTLINE

THEME

One of the most amazing aspects of the brain is the way it assembles itself. At a critical point, the maturing embryo develops a primitive neural plate, which is brought about by interaction between ectoderm and mesoderm. Each segment in this neural plate will ultimately form a specific structure in the brain. How the neural plate continues its growth and development to form the neural tube and subsequent structures in the brain is the subject of considerable research.

    No matter what part of the brain is being considered, cells go through the following stages in the embryological development of brain tissue:

1. Induction. Dividing cells form primitive neurons or glial cells through the interaction of ectoderm and mesoderm. Trophic factors are quite important in influencing the induction of neuronal tissue; in this case the trophic factors are believed to emanate from the mesoderm.

2. Proliferation. Proliferation refers to the division and multiplication of cells in particular regions of brain. The primitive cells from which neurons and glia originate give rise to many daughter cells as they cycle through their proliferative phase. In cortical and cerebellar tissues the germinal cells move from the outer to the inner surface of the cortex, dividing and multiplying with each cycle.

3. Migration. Once a daughter cell is produced, it migrates into its final location, using chemical and mechanical cues for guidance. The role of glial cells is quite important in cortical and cerebellar migration because the primitive neurons follow glial processes in their migration to their final destination.

4. Aggregation. Once in their final location, the cells aggregate, using cell surface recognition molecules, such as NCAM (neural cell adhesion molecules), to recognize the cells to join with.

5. Differentiation. The primitive cells then undergo differentiation into specific cell types that are unique to the structure being innervated. During this period of time the distinctive morphology and physiology of the cerebellar Purkinje cell, for example, is brought about. The process of differentiation almost certainly relies upon a significant readout of genetic information.

6. Circuit Formation. Once differentiated into a specific cell type, the circuits that are unique to this cell type are established. This involves the growth of dendritic and axonal extensions from the cell, guided by the growth cones which are responding in part to trophic factors such as nerve growth factor (NGF). The Nobel Prize was awarded to Levi-Montalcini for this discovery.

7. Synapse Formation. The establishment of synaptic contacts between the neuron and its target occurs at a rapid rate early in development. Modified by experience, synapse formation continues at a lower rate throughout life and may play a role in recovery of function from damage or even in the encoding of information in the nervous system.

8. **Cell Death.** During development excessive neurons proliferate and excessive synaptic contacts are created. The apparent failure of a neuron to achieve its target triggers that neuron to regress and die. Competition seems to be essential for the determination of cell death. The loser in a competition for a target--that is, a cell with non-functional synapses--is likely to be removed.

The process of neuronal development from the hollow blastocyst, containing one hundred cells at day five, to the fully developed nervous system, containing perhaps two hundred billion neurons by the first year of life, is one that is influenced both by genetic and environmental factors. The relationship between these two influences appears to be that the genes determine the range within which environmental influences can sculpt the developing nervous system. Development proceeds at a quite rapid pace in some regions of the brain. For example the cortical region of the telencephalon during its peak period of cellular proliferation gives birth to 250 thousand cells per minute. While this is an incredible number, it should also be remembered that 70% of all neurons are to be found in the telencephalon.

Sex and the Brain

The determination of the sex of an individual is under the control of X and Y chromosomes. The paired helical DNA of the female contains an X chromosome on each strand, whereas the corresponding male chromosome has an X on one strand and a Y on the other. When male and female strands recombine the resulting DNA strand will have either an XX (the female form) or an XY (the male form). In terms of brain sexual development and differentiation to male and female forms, it is the Y chromosome that is responsible for altering the brain away from the female condition. The Y chromosome induces testes formation, and testes, in turn, secrete the masculinizing hormone testosterone. In the absence of testosterone or the Y chromosome, the fetus remains in a female form. The gonadal hormones induce the secondary sexual characteristics typical of males and females. In terms of the overall control of sexual development it is important to recognize that the hormonal influences on the developing organism are part of the environmental influence, even though they are ultimately triggered by an inherited mechanism.

Brain sexual differences have been noted in a variety of species and are most pronounced in the brain of song canaries. In these species the male song is used for territorial establishment and mate selection. The song is brought about by testosterone, which induces morphological and functional changes in a specific song circuit of the brain. In humans it has been well established that there are male/female differences of the following variety: males are more aggressive and possess more acute visual spatial abilities, whereas females are more verbally fluent. The late Norman Geschwind has proposed a hypothesis wherein testosterone functions to delay left-hemisphere development in males. This hypothesis, which is somewhat controversial, does account for many of the male/female differences in human behavior and structure.

31

Studies of the effects of damage to the cortex in males and females indicate that laterality is more developed in the male brain. That is, damage to one hemisphere of the brain is more likely to result in a deficit in the male than it is in the female. Females have developed a more bilateral representation of function in the two hemispheres. Anatomical differences that exist between males and females are most notable in the corpus callosum and in the planum temporale. The anatomical differences in these regions of the brain have been related to some of the behavioral differences seen between males and females.

Sexual dysfunctions are known to exist among humans. Some of these are the result of errors in the genetic code. Turner's syndrome features an absence of the second sex chromosome (XO) and results in the absence of estradiol (the female sex hormone) and a resulting sterile individual possesses poorer visual spatial capabilities than other females. In Klinefelters' syndrome (XXY) an extra female chromosome is present in the genetic code. These males display some feminization as adults, yet have normal male visual-spatial skills.

Postnatal Development

Following birth the brain grows rapidly, attaining the bulk of it's growth in axons and dendrites (at birth, most neurons have already been generated). During early development, environmental influences act to sculpt the development of circuitry between neurons in connected regions of the brain. This can be seen dramatically and artifically with the surgical removal of a sensory apparatus, such as the removal of whiskers in the rodent and the correspondent alteration in cortical representation of whisker fields. Another dramatic and well studied form of postnatal plasticity can be seen in a variety of studies manipulating the visual system to alter such properties as binocularity and orientation preference.

Such alterations in sensory experience do not often occur in humans, but when they do occur the behavioral results are very similar to that seen with animal preparations. The studies reported in Iran in which infants were cared for in restricted environments points up the necessity for the interaction of environment influences with the genetic code to optimally tune the nervous system for the environment in which the organism find itself. Studies of enriched environments in rodents have shown significant changes in the amount of cortical tissue, synapses, and neurotransmitters, following even a brief exposure to an enriched environment.

Aging

As aging occurs in the nervous system, do individuals lose intellectual and cognitive capabilities? For many years the data suggested that the performance in an aged human deteriorates, perhaps due to problems of neuronal processing of cognitive information. In recent years it has become apparent that many of the factors leading to lower scores among the aged relate more to deficiencies in sensory processing (eyesight and hearing may decline) but that if speed of response is not a criterion for performance, the aged individual shows no decline in cognitive/intellectual capabilities. Certainly changes are occurring in the brain such that by the eightieth year of life approximately 10% of the weight of the brain has been lost. Much of this loss is the result of neurons that die for one reason or another. The brain apparently attempts to compensate for this loss by growing synapses on the surviving dendrites.

As the population of this country grows older, the problems associated with dementia will become more severe. It is now estimated that five percent of the population over the age of 65 experiences some form of dementia, with one or two percent of individuals possessing a severe case.

In most cases dementia has been traced to the selective degeneration of particular kinds of neurons, but the causes are not always clear. There does seem to be a significant genetic component in many aspects of dementia leading to the idea that a genetic predisposition to a particular cell degeneration may be expressed via exposure to an environmental toxin or stressor.

The development of the central nervous system and its functions represent a wondrous process that scientists only dimly appreciate at present. The means by which billions of neurons can assume their final position to interact with their appropriate targets is only poorly understood currently. How the nervous system, once its final pattern is established, is capable of taking on all of the properties that we assume and take for granted on a daily basis represents a fundamental challenge for understanding how processes of perception, motivation, memory, and creativity can be accomplished with the cellular elements and systems that you have learned about in this course.

QUESTIONS TO KEEP IN MIND AS YOU READ THIS CHAPTER

1. The processes that guide brain development appear to be the same for all neurons regardless of their location. What are the forces acting upon the developing neuron to guide to its final destination and to its final targets?

2. How can the phenomenon of cell death improve a developing nervous system?

3. The text makes the point that the behavioral differences seen between males and females result from differences between the brains of males and females. Based on this argument do you think it fair to assume that the differences in other aspects of behavior between individuals will be reflected in changes in brain structure and function between these individuals?

4. Why is the brain composed of a variety of different structures? Why is it not a more uniform structure, as is muscle for example?

5. There are known differences in cerebral laterality between males and females. Can you relate these differences to any selective pressures that may have operated earlier in our development?

STUDENT'S OUTLINE

After you have read this chapter and studied the material it contains close the book and, in the space below, using your own words, try to outline the major points that you have just read. The basic structure of the chapter is provided below.

Prenatal development

Sex and the brain

Postnatal   development

Aging and the brain

Development of brain and mind

Now that you have attempted to outline this chapter from memory go back to the textbook and see how accurate your recollection was, fill-in those topics you might have missed, and emphasize the points that are stressed in the textbook.

Key Terms

The following terms are introduced in this chapter (the terms are defined in the textbook). You should be sure that you know these terms and can define them.

Activational effects
Aggregation
Autosomal dominant disorders
Blastocyst
Differentiation
Dimorphism
Ectoderm
Embryonic disc

Filopodia
Follicle
Growth cone
Ideopathic hypogonadotrophic hypogonadism
Induction
Intermediate zone
Klinefelter's syndrome
Lipofuscin
Marginal zone
Meiosis
Mesoderm
Migration
Mitosis
Nerve-growth factor (NGF)
Neural crest
Neural plate
Neural tube
Neuroblast
Organizational effects
Plasticity
Proliferation
Substrate
Subventricular zone
Trophic factors
Turner's syndrome
Ventricular zone

Multiple Choice

1. By the fifth day after fertilization, the original cell has divided until there are about
   a. 10 embryonic cells
   b. 100 embryonic cells
   c. 1,000 embryonic cells
   d. 10,000 embryonic cells

2. The embryonic disc is composed of
   a. mesoderm and ectoderm
   b. neurons and glia
   c. ectoderm and endoderm
   d. the neural plate and neural tube

3. Which of the following is NOT generated from the ectoderm layer of the embryonic disc
   a. muscle
   b. brain
   c. skin
   d. hair

4. The forebrain is composed of
   a. hypothalamus and brainstem
   b. brainstem and diencephalon
   c. cerebellum and cortex
   d. telencephalon and diencephalon

5. Neuroscientists believe that the process that leads to the induction of specific cell types (neurons vs. bone cells) involves
   a. an interaction between ectoderm and mesoderm
   b. the transfer of trophic factors from mesoderm to ectoderm
   c. both a and b
   d. neither a or b

6. During the proliferation stage of developement, cells
   a. are totally under genetic guidance, dividing every 3 seconds
   b. migrate between the endoderm and ectoderm
   c. oscillate between the marginal zone and the ventricular zone
   d. first move to their final locations, then divide

7. The absence of glial cells during early stages of neuronal proliferation and migration would affect developing neurons in the following way:
   a. more cells would develop into neurons
   b. neurons would not be able to migrate to their proper locations
   c. fewer neurons would be induced without factors secreted by glial cells
   d. the lack of glial cells would not affect neuronal development

8. The general rule that holds throughout development of the nervous system is
   a. the brain is built under the sole direction of the genetic code
   b. once proliferated, the final destiny of neurons is solely determined by the cellular environment
   c. brain development is a product of the interaction between genetic information and the cellular enviroment
   d. The environment determines the overall specifications for the nervous system, and the genetic code fine tunes the resultant neuronal circuit.

9. Axons of neurons generally find their synaptic targets by using the following process:
   a. growth cones follow chemical gradients
   b. the direction of an axon is determined by DNA
   c. they randomly synapse with targets of opportunity
   d. after synapsing to the nearest vacant target, the neuron assumes the properties of its target

10. Which of the following is the correct designation for the male sex chromosome Klinefelters — males
    a. XXY
    b. XX Female Turners Syndrome - sterile
    c. XO
    d. XY Male

11. The default condition of the body is the female form. Which of the following is necessary for the development of the male form
    a. testosterone
    b. estrogen
    c. a "male" social environment
    d. progesterone

12. Which statement about the brains of male and female humans is most accurate
    a. the male cerebral cortex is larger than the female cortex
    b. there are no reliable differences based upon sex
    c. the female corpus callosum is larger than that of the male
    d. the male language cortex is larger than that of the female

13. The development of visual cortical dominance columns
    a. shows the establishment of cortical processing by genetic factors
    b. reflects competition between neurons from each of the eyes
    c. is unaffected by visual experience
    d. appears shortly before birth

14. Which of the following statements is most correct with respect to the role of the environment in brain development
    a.   the environment plays a role only in the development of sensory systems
    b.   genetic endowments alone are responsible for brain development
    c.   normal experience stimulates brain development
    d.   cell death is a result of environmental influences

15. Alzheimer's Disease
    a.   is a degenerative disease of the brain
    b.   cannot be cured
    c.   results in plaques and tangles in brain tissue
    d.   all the above

True-False

____1.   During development, the most indespensible organs--the heart and the brain--begin to form first.

____2.   Early in development it is possible to remove tiny portions of the neural plate and still form a complete brain.

____3.   Between 90-95% of the neurons of the brain are in the cerebral cortex.

____4.   At its maximum growth rate, the cerebral cortex adds about 250,000 cells per minute.

____5.   The formation of clusters of similar neurons (nuclei) is thought to depend upon specific cell-surface molecules such as NCAM.

____6.   Across cultures males are no more aggressive than females.

____7.   On average, females are more verbally fluent than males.

____8.   On average, females have more acute visual-spatial abilities than males.

____9.   For most people the parts of the brain responsible for language are distributed equally between left and right hemispheres.

____10. The human brain reaches half its adult size by six months of age.

____11. For the most part, neurons continue to divide until puberty.

____12. Rats raised in enriched environments grew more synapses on their cortical neurons.

_F_ 13. In healthly old people, the brain has lost 50% of its weight by age 90.

_F_ 14. Normally, neurons that die are replaced.

_T_ 15. Prenatally, hormones have an organizing effect on the brain.

Matching

_D_ 1.	neuroblasts	A.	language cortex
_G_ 2.	peripheral ANS	B.	the growing tip of an axon
_C_ 3.	marginal zone	C.	outer surface of neuronal tube
_J_ 4.	ventricular zone	D.	young neurons
_B_ 5.	filopodia	E.	degenerating neurons
_I_ 6.	NGF	F.	inside-out
_H_ 7.	Klinefelter's Syndrome	G.	neuronal crest
_E_ 8.	Alzheimer's Disease	H.	XXY
_A_ 9.	planum temporale	I.	guidance in peripheral nervous system development
_F_ 10.	development of neocortex	J.	location of neuronal mitosis

Short Answer

1. Describe the effects of raising an animal in complete darkness. What effect does this have on the developing visual system? Are any effects of raising an animal in darkness permanent?

2. Follow the "life history" of a single neuron from birth to death. What factors influence its development and survival?

3. Consider the role that hormones play in brain development generally and sexual differentiation specifically.

4. What evolutionary pressures may have occurred to result in the sexual differentiation of the human brain?

5. Consider the implications of the experiments removing the whiskers of young mice.

ANSWERS TO SELF-TEST

Multiple Choice

1. b	2. c	3. a	4. d	5. c	6. c	7. b
8. c	9. a	10. d	11. a	12. c	13. b	14. c
15. d						

True or False

1. T	2. T	3. F	4. T	5. T	6. F	7. T
8. F	9. F	10. T	11. F	12. T	13. F	14. F
15. T						

Matching

1. D
2. G
3. C
4. J
5. B
6. I
7. H
8. E
9. A
10. F

CHAPTER 4
SENSING AND MOVING

Before You Read This Chapter

OBJECTIVES

After reading this chapter, you should be able to do the following:

1. Understand the anatomy and physiology of brain sensory systems.

2. Know the process by which information is extracted from sensory signals and transmitted to other areas for further abstraction, finally culminating in perception.

3. Be aware of the features common to all sensory systems.

4. Understand the kinds of physical stimuli to which the sensory system is responsive.

5. Appreciate that sensory systems process the following kinds of information: (a) time, (b) location, (c) stimulus quality, (d) stimulus quantity.

6. Know that sensory events exist only in coded patterns of nerve impulses within the brain. The processes of sensation and perception are the reconstruction of the external world by various brain systems.

7. Understand the receptive field properties of sensory systems.

8. The role of reflexes is of importance in understanding motor function. Be familiar with the local control of muscle activity and the common reflexes.

9. Explain the role of the motor cortex in initiating movement.

10. The basal ganglia and cerebellum participate in movement in a "modulatory manner." Be able to depict the role of these two structure in movement.

OUTLINE

A general model for the sensing systems

What do we sense
Fine tuning of the receptive process

Sensing: A detailed look at the visual system

The structure of the visual system
The eye
The optic nerve and optic tract
The lateral geniculate nucleus
The superior colliculus
The visual areas of the cerebral cortex
Cortical representation of vision
Signal processing properties of cortical neurons
Neurons that respond selectively to visual features
Two eyes: one world
Color: the special quality of vision
Object vision and spatial vision

How general is parallel processing?

Hearing: A brief look at the auditory system

What sound is
The structure of the ear
Pathways from ear to auditory cortex
Neural coding of sound
Pitch
Loudness
Location
Feature detection

Taste and smell: A brief look

Taste
Smell

Moving

Muscles and joints
The spinal cord
Spinal reflexes
Reciprocal control principles
The motor cortex
The basal ganglia
The cerebellum

Review and conclusions

THEME

In this chapter we consider two areas of the neurosciences in which a great deal of information is known: sensory systems and motor systems. In an effort to cope with the tremendous scientific literature that exists regarding the sensory and motor systems, the authors of this text have chosen to emphasize one system in detail--the visual system. From an understanding of the visual system, it is possible to extract common principles that are applicable to all sensory systems. In addition, the principles that govern sensory system operation, in reverse, hold true for much of the function of motor systems.

General Model for Sensing Systems

A full appreciation of the functioning of sensory and motor systems requires an understanding of their anatomy. Therefore it might be advisable for you to go back and review some salient aspects of brain anatomy in Chapters 1 and 2 in preparation for this chapter.

A sensory system has two requirements to be effective; it must be able to convert (transduce) sensory stimuli into nervous impulses; and the brain must possess the circuitry to analyze and make sense of the patterns that impinge on the sensory receptors. The brain does this by employing specific sensory receptors that respond best to light, to sound, and to other sensory modalities that we can detect. This information is then subjected to an extensive analysis to extract the "meaning" of the sensory pattern. The brain accomplishes this extraction by utilizing "feature detectors," which are neuronal circuits designed to respond to certain aspects of the sensory stimulus. As one proceeds deeper and deeper into the circuitry of the brain, the extraction process becomes more and more sophisticated.

But what happens at the end? How does all this sensory information wind up being perceived as an object in the environment? We might suppose that all this information eventually filters down to one or a few cells which, when activated, represent the object in the environment. While perhaps a logical possibility, this is not the way the nervous system encodes sensory information. Rather than a single location, many regions in the sensory portions of the brain are activated so that the pattern of neuronal activity elicited by the sensory event becomes the neural representation of that event or object. This implies that there does not exist within the brain a "little man" whose function is to "read" the pattern of activation and decide what it is that is being seen. The pattern of activation itself is the neural representation of the event or object.

Sensory systems require a minimum number of components in order to be effective. These components consist of a stimulus detector to transduce physical energy into neural impulses, an initial receiving center where neurons receive convergent information from groups of sensory receptors, and one or more secondary receiving and integrating centers where neurons receive information from groups of secondary receiving centers. As you can see, this is a hierarchical arrangement in which the function of one center depends upon the receipt of pre-processed information from a "lower" center. The end point of this chain of processing is the conscious identification, called perception, of the stimulus event. The human nervous system is specialized to respond to the following varieties of sensory information: vision, hearing, touch, taste, smell, and gravity. Other organisms possess sensory systems specialized to respond to other forms of physical energy. For example, some insects can sense polarized light (bees), other animals can hear very low frequency sound (whales), and still others can respond to ultrasound (bats). These different sensory abilities are made possible by the existence of different classes of sensory transducers and brain circuits.

All forms of sensory systems carry information about (a) time-- when the stimulus began and how long it lasted; (b) the quality of the stimulus--the color of a visual object or the temperature of a tactile object; and (c) the quantity of the stimulus--the brightness of a light or the loudness of a sound. All these features of the sensory signal are encoded in terms of the activity of neurons along the processing pathways.

The Nature of the Sensory Response

Most, but not all, sensory receptors respond best to a changing stimulus. The nature of the sensory receptor causes it to diminish its response to a constant stimulus. This process is known as "adaptation" and should be distinguished from a phenomenon termed "habituation" that you will encounter in Chapter 8. Adaptation is a property of the sensory receptor itself, whose response to a constant stimulus declines with time. In habituation, the declining response to a stimulus is a property of neurons inside the central nervous system and not a property of the sensory receptor. From an adaptive point of view, sensory adaptation makes sense in that a continuous stimulus may not convey as much relevant information to an organism as one that is novel or changing. You may object to this reasoning since visual images do not fade away when you stare at them for a long period of time. The reason for this is that imperceptible motions of the eyeball are continually occurring so that the image projected onto the retina is, in fact, continually changing. Experiments that have attempted to stabilize the image on the retina have shown that, under these conditions, one's perception of an object does fade away.

It is important to note that our perception of the physical world exists only in coded patterns of nerve impulses within specific sensory channels in the brain. Strangely enough, stimuli do not have to be physically present in order for a perception to occur. Every night we dream and experience vivid perceptions of objects and events that are not there. A hallucination induced by alcohol or mental illness likewise appears real to the individual, who may resist believing that the events or objects are not really present.

The brain possesses specific channels for each sensory system. Table 4.2 lists the six human senses and channels in the brain that these systems utilize. In many cases, sensory processing can be quite complex; rather than a simple linear sequence, they resemble a multiple parallel processing systems. For example, in vision, hearing, and touch, it is known that there exist multiple cortical processing regions for each of these sensory modalities. The different cortical processing areas are apparently involved in different aspects of analysis of the sensory event.

It is important to recognize that the existence of several levels of processing, each of which involves synaptic relays, implies that processing occurs at each of the sensory nuclei. The term "relay nuclei" creates the impression that the information is simply relayed or passed through the structure without modification. A moment's reflection, however, will indicate that if the goal is to simply pass the information through the brain, one would not require a synapse because an axon could do the job more efficiently. Therefore, the presence of relay nuclei and the synaptic processing that occurs in these nuclei imply signal processing at each stage. The circuits involved in sensory relay systems are primarily hierarchical circuits that connect various levels of a sensory system and local circuits that operate within each level. You may wish to refer back to Chapter 2 for a review of the principles of operation of these two basic kinds of neuronal circuits.

Receptive Fields

An important concept in sensory systems refers to the "receptive field" of an element. By receptive field is meant the portion of the sensory world to which that element responds. In the visual system, for example, a single visual receptor in the retina is active only when that cell's receptive field is active. As one progresses further into the brain, the neurons change their receptive field properties. Much of the pioneering work in the last two decades has been directed to understanding the receptive field characteristics of neurons at various levels of the brain and how those receptive fields are structured. For example, in the visual system, if one looks at the receptive field properties of cells in the visual cortex (as opposed to receptor cells in the retina), one finds that the cortical cell responds to a pattern of light input as opposed to a spot of light. Some cells in the visual cortex respond preferentially to a line, whereas other cells in the visual cortex respond best to an angle moving through the visual field. Both are examples of more complex receptive field properties.

Visual input enters the eye through the cornea and lens, which work together to focus the image onto the retina. Within the retina are found the sensory receptor cells--the rods and cones--as well as four other varieties of neurons (bipolar, ganglion, horizontal, amacrine). The presence of so much circuitry in the retina is unusual in that outside the confines of the brain most other sensory systems do not possess a rich array of processing capabilities. In this respect, the retina of the eye is considered an extension of the brain. Neurologists and ophthalmologists take advantage of this feature, and by looking into your eye during a physical examination, they can learn something about the brain by examining the surface of the retina.

The Visual System

Most people are aware of cameras that are so automatic that the user no longer needs to focus the lens. How is it that the eye is capable of altering the shape of the lens to correctly focus the image on the surface of the retina? Cameras utilize devices to measure the distance of the object, but the eye possesses a much more sophisticated mechanism that analyzes the "focus" of the image in the occipital cortex. Although we take for granted the ability to focus or accommodate, the actual adjustments required are quite remarkable. For example, not only does the lens need to alter its shape, depending upon the distance of the object, but the iris changes its diameter both as a function of distance and as a function of light intensity. Furthermore, when the object is relatively close, both eyes must pivot toward one another so that they are both aimed at the object. All these adjustments occur without our awareness and represent good examples of a homeostatic mechanism (homeostasis is discussed in more detail in Chapter 5).

It is a general property of sensory and motor systems that information from the right side of the body is represented in the left side of the brain and vice versa. The visual system is no exception to this general rule. Images from the left half of visual space are represented in the right hemisphere, and images from the right half of visual space are represented in the left hemisphere. Since each eye can register images from both the left half and the right half of visual space, the axons from the respective ganglion cells in each retina must take a different course, some projecting into the left side of the brain and others into the right side. You should review the anatomy of the visual system to make sure that you understand this feature. Be careful not to let the fact that the lens reverses images in the eye confuse you. Images in the right visual field project onto the left side of the eyeball and, in turn, are carried to the left side of the brain. The anatomical structures responsible include the optic nerve, optic chiasm, optic trace, superior colliculus, lateral geniculate nucleus, optic radiation and primary visual cortex.

Brain Processing of Retinal Information

The optic tract has four targets in the brain: the lateral geniculate nucleus, the superior colliculus, the superchiasmatic nucleus and the oculomotor nucleus. Most is known by far about the projections to the lateral geniculate nucleus and the superior colliculus. The lateral geniculate nucleus is the visual relay in the thalamus for fibers en route to the primary visual cortex. The superior colliculus is the target of some ganglion cells and is concerned with visual reflexes and with integrating information that we use to orient ourselves spatially in a moving world. The projections to the superchiasmatic nucleus are important in circadian rhythms (see Chapter 6), while the oculomotor nuclei are an important homeostatic component that keeps the movements of the eye coordinated as we look at moving objects.

A great deal of research has been done on the function of the primary visual cortex, which is also known as striate cortex, area VI, and area 17. As mentioned earlier, the visual system has more than one primary processing area in the cortex. The three areas that have been most extensively studied are areas 17, 18, and 19. (These numbers refer to distinctions made between regions of the cortex based on a microscopic examination of its anatomy.) Area 17 is the primary visual cortex, while areas 18 and 19 are termed secondary visual cortex. All of these areas, and more, are richly interconnected. Within the cortex, cells are arranged in columns. These vertically aligned columns of cells act together in processing similar kinds of information. In a classic series of experiments, David Hubel and Torsten Wiesel discovered that cells within a column display the same orientation preferences. Recall that neurons making up a single visual column all respond to lines having the same orientation in space (a horizontal line, for instance). When one examines the cells from an adjacent column, one finds that the preferred angle of orientation has changed slightly in a clockwise or counterclockwise direction. If extensive maps are made of the orientation preferences of cells throughout the visual cortex, one finds an orderly relationship between adjacent columns. It is almost as if aspects of the visual world were being mapped upon the visual cortex. In contrast, the receptive field properties of cells in the lateral geniculate nucleus were found not to display such complex receptive field properties. Rather, they respond optimally to visual stimuli that are shaped like doughnuts or doughnut holes.

We have seen how the visual system is capable of extracting information by means of cell responses. How might these features be represented in the brain? One possible answer is that there are processing centers that further abstract the visual stimulus. An experiment by Charles Gross serves to illuminate one such possibility. While recording from single neurons in a secondary visual area of the monkey, Gross observed that the neuron's preferred stimulus was the silhouette of a monkey's hand. Similar studies were done in which it was found that single neurons responded optimally to drawings of the face of a monkey. One possible interpretation of these findings is that many neurons with simpler receptive field characteristics are converging upon these "hand" or "face" neurons, causing them to fire when the appropriate stimulus appears. Does this observation violate our earlier conclusion that information is widely represented in the brain as opposed to being represented in single cells? While we cannot know the answer with certainty because we are unable to record information from even a tiny population of the billions of neurons in the brain at any one time, these findings do suggest that what we are seeing is the cumulative result of a tremendous amount of hierarchical feature extraction. One problem that is always encountered in these experiments is that one cannot be sure that the optimal stimulus for any one cell or group of cells has been presented. Obviously, one cannot present an infinite number of stimulus objects and the possibility always exists that the "truly optimal stimulus" has been missed.

How is the visual information from both of our eyes represented in the brain? Nerve fibers from equivalent portions of the visual field of the two eyes can be traced across their geniculate connections all the way to the visual cortex. In the visual cortex, the right and left eye projections form alternating "ocular dominance" columns or strips throughout the visual cortex. Through the complex interaction between ocular dominance columns arises the ability to see the world in three dimensions. The textbook discusses some surprising facts about cortical organization that have become apparent by depriving one eye of light from birth and seeing what happens to the organization of visual cortex. These results indicate that a certain environment is needed in order to fully develop the capabilities built into our visual system, and, by extension, into our whole brain.

There are two kinds of sensory receptors in the retina: rods and cones. The rods are responsible for twilight vision, which is poor in detail and lacks color but is very sensitive; the cones are responsible for high acuity form and detail vision and for color vision. The neuronal circuitry of the retina gives rise to our ability to see the four primary colors of red, yellow, blue, and green.

Research into the circuitry of the visual system has demonstrated the existence of two parallel systems of visual analysis that operate to discriminate spatial as opposed to object information. Each system uses different combinations of cell circuitry. The end result of these two systems is to complete the analysis of the visual world. Many other sensory systems also employ parallel processing in their analysis of the sensory world. By keeping our analysis of primary sensory information separate and parallel, we increase our capacity for analytical operations. A system designed to process information "serially" would be much too slow to keep up with a rapidly changing stimulus.

The Auditory System

The auditory system is specifically designed to transduce vibrations of air molecules into tiny patterns of movement of the ossicles of the middle ear. One of the problems facing a system to translate vibrations of air molecules into vibrations of the fluid-filled inner ear is that considerably more energy is required to create motion in fluid as opposed to motion in air molecules. The middle ear ossicles act as tiny levers to convert the relatively high-amplitude, low-power auditory vibrations into low-amplitude, high-power fluid vibrations.

The auditory system is somewhat different than the visual system in that auditory information is largely sequential whereas visual information tends to be simultaneous. The analysis of a visual scene is grasped instantaneously by the relationships between environmental objects at any point in time. Auditory information however, is generally understood only by integrating auditory signals over a period of time and then making sense of them. For example, language understanding can only be done by determining the context in which words are being uttered.

You should recognize the parallels between the visual system and the auditory system. Both systems must transduce physical forms of energy (photons, molecular vibrations in the air) into neural signals. The sensory impulses are then sent to higher processing relay stations in the brain via parallel pathways of axons. Preserved through the relay stations of the brain is information related to the "receptor-topic" nature of the sensory system, the retinal projection with respect to the visual system and the cochlear projection with respect to the auditory system. In turn, this receptortopic information is projected onto the visual and auditory primary receiving areas of cortex. And, in manner analogous to the strategy employed by neurons in the visual system, neurons of the auditory systems extract certain features from the incoming auditory signal and respond best to unique aspects of auditory coding. The auditory pathway, of course, is totally separate from the visual one, the major structures being the cochlear nucleus, superior olivary nuclei, inferior colliculus, lateral geniculate nucleus, and primary auditory cortex.

The Chemical Senses

Major differences can be seen by considering the chemical senses of taste and smell which appear to operate by the establishment of a number of categories which are relatively activated by various chemicals in the food we eat or the air we breathe. While perhaps not as important a sense in human experience, both taste and smell are quite important to many animals aside from humans and appear to occupy a unique role in the evolution of the brain, particularly with respect to the limbic system. The anatomy of the taste system includes the chorda tympani, glossopharyngeal nerve, vagus nerve, nucleus of the solitary tract, arcuate nucleus, and somatosensory cortex. The olfactory system depends upon the olfactory epithelium, bulbs, and tracts, and mitral cells which project to the piriform cortex.

Moving

We now turn our attention to motor systems of the brain. In order to move a limb in two different directions (extension and contraction), two different muscles are required. A general rule of the motor system is that every muscle that pulls in one direction is opposed by another muscle that pulls in the opposite direction.

Muscles are activated by nerves that release acetylcholine, which transmits the signal to contract to the muscle. Acetylcholine is found in a wide variety of regions in the central nervous system. Acetylcholine neurotransmitter released at a nerve-muscle junction acts upon receptors on the muscle surface to trigger process of contraction. The cell body that supplies the axon innervating the muscle is found either in the spinal cord or in the brain stem. These neurons, called motor neurons, are also known as the "final common path" for movement, because any preceding brain activity must ultimately express itself through these neurons. A single motor neuron in the brain stem or spinal cord can supply many different muscle fibers within a muscle. The motor neuron and the muscle fibers that it controls are called the "motor unit." A motor neuron supplying muscles in the back or thigh may innervate hundreds of muscle fibers, whereas one innervating the fingers or tongue may innervate only a few. The latter are, as a result, capable of quite fine and detailed movement, whereas the former lack precision and make up for it with increased contractile strength.

Much of the activity of the musculature occurs without conscious awareness. Many of our movements are made up of reflexes that are controlled by the spinal cord, which contains enough "programming" to permit rhythmic walking and other forms of coordinated motor activity in the absence of input from the brain. These internally wired local systems of the spinal cord control many walking adjustments quite automatically once movement is initiated from higher brain regions.

The part of the cortex that initiates movement is known as the motor cortex. Located in the frontal lobes, the motor cortex projects by means of the pyramidal tracts into the spinal cord, where synapses are made ultimately upon motor neurons. The motor cortex codes our movements not by instructing a series of muscles to contract in the proper order but by desired joint position, which is then carried out by subordinate circuitry in the spinal cord and elsewhere.

A second motor system is involved in smoothing out and coordinating voluntary motor movement. The brain structures involved in this motor modulation are the basal ganglia and the cerebellum. Both of these structures work to coordinate the movement of body musculature and to adjust the activity of the motor cortex and the spinal cord by using feedback signals to produce smooth and coordinated motion. In addition, the cerebellum determines where the parts of the body are at any moment and compares where a body part is relative to where it should be.

Parkinson's disease is a condition in which dopamine-containing neurons of the substantia nigra die. These cells normally project to the basal ganglia and are involved in motor modulation. In patients with Parkinson's disease, the basal ganglia are deficient in dopamine and, as a result, motor disturbances in the form of tremors and an inability to initiate voluntary movement are present. Patients can be successfully treated for Parkinson's disease with the drug L-DOPA, which makes up for their declining stores of dopamine. However, the treatment is not a cure but merely provides symptomatic relief.

Sensory and Motor Function

In this chapter we have examined sensory and motor systems of the brain. We have seen that many sensory systems utilize the same general principles in their operation. All employ sensory receptors that function to transduce physical stimuli into neural impulses. All employ several stages of processing and information extraction at various levels throughout the brain.

We have chosen to focus upon the visual system for a detailed analysis of the brain substrates of sensation. We know a good deal about the visual system and can describe many of the cellular activities at the levels of the retina, the lateral geniculate and the visual cortex. It is known that cells in these structures operate as feature detectors, extracting salient information from the sensory input. As one proceeds further into the sensory processing capabilities of the brain, the nature of the feature extraction by individual neurons becomes more and more sophisticated. We have seen that the characteristics of the human visual system, including such things as depth perception, color vision and form perception, are emergent functions of its cellular processes and neuronal circuitry. The visual system, as well as other sensory modalities, employs parallel processing circuits that are specialized for the analysis of the various properties of physical stimuli such as movement, color, form, and location.

The function of the motor system is, of course, to regulate muscular contraction, but more importantly to control the position of limbs and other body structures in space. Two brain systems are involved in the control of movement. The motor cortex of the frontal lobe is the site of voluntary commands designed to position parts of the body accurately in space. Information from the motor cortex is routed via the pyramidal system to motor neurons in the brainstem and spinal cord, where eventually synaptic contact is made with muscle fibers. The second brain system involved in movement is composed of the basal ganglia and cerebellum, both of which modulate the activity of the pyramidal system. The motor modulating system permits smooth, coordinated movements among the various muscle groups and provides feedback to the motor cortex to regulate neural commands leading to muscular contraction.

Because of the relative ease with which scientists can study the sensory and motor systems (it is easier to study input and output systems in experimental animals than the intervening processing systems), we have amassed a great deal of knowledge about their operation from a cellular and a neuronal circuit perspective. Most of the human brain is devoted to functions other than sensation and movement. It will be our task in succeeding chapters to begin an analysis of the brain processes that account for such phenomena as emotions, learning, memory, thinking, consciousness, and mental illness.

QUESTIONS TO KEEP IN MIND AS YOU READ THIS CHAPTER

1. What are the stimuli to which humans are capable of responding and how is it that other species can respond to other forms of stimulation?

2. To what degree is our perception of the visual world dependent upon the processing abilities of the brain?

3. What role does experience have in determining our perception of the world?

4. What components of the brain are involved in sensory processing?

5. Is it possible to imagine what other species experience when responding to other forms of physical energy?

6. We tend to view things such as walking, throwing a ball and engaging in athletics as "voluntary activities," but to what extent to you consciously think of the movements of each of the muscles in your body during these activities?

7. What are the commonalties, as well as differences, between the anatomical structure and physiological function of the various sensory systems.

After You Have Read the Chapter, Continue with the Following

STUDENT'S OUTLINE

After you have read this chapter and studied the material it contains, close the book and in the space below, using your own words, try to outline the major points you have just read. The basic structure of the chapter is provided below.

A general model for the sensing systems

Sensing: A detailed look at the visual system

How general is parallel processing?

Hearing: A brief look at the auditory system

Taste and smell: A brief look

Moving

Review and conclusions

Now that you have attempted to outline this chapter from memory, go back to the textbook and see how accurate your recollection was. Fill in those topics you might have missed and emphasize the points that are stressed in the textbook.

Key Terms

The following terms were introduced in this chapter. Be sure that you know these terms and can define them.

Accommodation
Adaptation
Amacrine cells
Amyotrophic lateral sclerosis
Astigmatism
Audition
Auditory nerve
Basilar membrane
Betz cells
Bipolar neurons
Cataract
Chorda tympani
Cochlea
Cochlear canal
Cochlear nerve
Cone
Cornea
Deep cerebellar nuclei
External auditory canal
Fovea
Ganglion cells
Glaucoma
Glossopharyngeal nerve
Granule-cell neurons
Gustation
Hair cells
Horizontal cells
Hyperopia
Incus
Inferior colliculi
Iris
Lateral geniculate nucleus
Lens
Malleus
Motor neuron
Multiple sclerosis
Myasthenia gravis
Myopia
Nucleus of the solitary tract
Ocular dominance columns
Olfaction
Opponent-process theory
Optic chiasm
Optic nerve
Optic tract
Organ of Corti
Ossicles
Oval window
Papillae

Parkinson's disease
Pinna
Pitch
Primary visual cortex
Proprioception
Pupil
Pulvinar
Purkinje cells
Pyramidal tract
Receptive field
Reissner's membrane
Retina
Retinotopic organization
Rods
Round window
Somatic sensation
Stapes
Superior colliculi
Tectorial membrane
Timbre
Tympanic canal
Tympanic membrane
Vestibular apparatus
Vestibular canal

SELF TEST

Multiple Choice

1. The initial receiving center is the component of the sensory system that
   a. receives information from the external environment
   b. consists of a specialized receptor neuron
   c. sends information to the cortex
   d. receives information from groups of detector units

2. A stimulus detector converts a sensory event from its original physical form into
   a. neurotransmitter chemicals
   b. action potentials
   c. modulatory peptides
   d. none of the above

3. Which of the following is NOT a quality distinguished by its own sensory receptor
   a. tone
   b. temperature
   c. pain
   d. color

4. Which of the following is NOT a quality distinguished by the sense of taste
   a. fruity
   b. sweet
   c. bitter
   d. salt

5. The shape of the lens varies from thin and flat to thick and round depending on
   a. the amount of light being reflected from the object under inspection
   b. the distance between the object and the viewer
   c. the amount of constriction or relaxation in the iris
   d. the distance between the retina and the lens

6. Accommodation is
   a. the change in the size of the pupil with exposure to different light intensities
   b. the adjustments made in both the pupil and the lens in order to focus upon either near or far objects
   c. the ability to compensate for a retina that is either too close or too far from the lens
   d. none of the above

7. Which of the following types of neurons are NOT found in the retina
   a. bipolar cells
   b. horizontal cells
   c. amacrine cells
   d. Purkinje cells

8. Cones are most dense on which part of the retina
   a. the blind spot
   b. the fovea
   c. the periphery
   d. they are evenly distributed over the retina

9. Within the optic chiasm
   a. information from the nasal half of both retinae crosses to the opposite side of the brain
   b. information from the temporal half of both retaine crosses to the opposite side of the brain
   c. the optic nerves decussate
   d. the optic tracts decussate

10. Simple cortical cells are most likely to be activated by
    a. movement of light through the visual field
    b. dark edges within the visual field
    c. orientation of a bar in visual space
    d. none of the above

11. Analysis of the pigments contained in cones reveals that one type of cone exists for which of the following
    a. light at wavelengths representing red, yellow and blue
    b. light at wavelengths representing blue, green and yellow
    c. light at wavelengths representing blue, red and green
    d. light at all wavelengths in the visual spectrum

depends on pattern of excitation

12. The number of muscle fibers controlled by a given motor neuron varies, depending on
    a. the amount of strength which the muscle needs to produce
    b. the size of the muscle
    c. how coarse or fine the muscle movements need to be
    d. how far from the motoneuron its fiber must travel

13. Muscle fibers contain sensory nerves that represent the sense of
    a. proprioception
    b. nociception
    c. olfaction
    d. none of the above

14. Reflexes represent a class of responses that
    a. do not involve a loop from sensation to activation
    b. are processed exclusively within the spinal cord
    c. are voluntary movements
    d. must be integrated at the level of the brainstem

15. It is currently believed that the primary function of the cortical motor column is
    a. to activate specific related muscles
    b. to achieve a specific joint position
    c. to control involuntary movement
    d. to integrate reciprocal muscle controls

True or False

___T___ 1. Myasthenia gravis is an autoimmune disorder of the muscle acetylcholine receptor *ACh*

___F___ 2. Motor cells control muscles in a one-to-one relationship. *sensory*

___T___ 3. All forms of sensing carry information about time. *location stimulus quality, quantity*

___F___ 4. The sensory system subserving the modality of audition is the hair cell. *fund*

___T___ 5. Sensory receptors act to translate external physical stimuli into action potentials.

___T___ 6. The retina contains both stimulus detectors and an initial receiving center.

F ___ 7. Divergent information channeling allows enhanced spatial resolution of sensation but reduces the ability to detect the sensation.

F ___ 8. By altering the size and shape of the pupil, the iris acts to focus images upon the retina.

F ___ 9. The retinal cells that send their axons to the lateral geniculate nucleus are the bipolar cells.

T ___ 10. The retinal layer that faces incoming light consists of ganglion cell axons.

F ___ 11. Cortical events are processed locally within horizontal *vertical* planes.

F ___ 12. One kind of rod exists for each of three primary colors.

T ___ 13. Most muscles connect two bones across the joint they share in common.

F ___ 14. The action of acetylcholine at its receptor is opposed by nicotine.

T ___ 15. A motor unit consists of a motor neuron, its axon and the muscle it controls.

Matching

A. Match the following action or sensation to the highest relay level with which it is associated.

c ___ vision		a.	somatosensory cortex — *taste*
f ___ hearing		b.	motor cortex — *voluntary mvmt*
a ___ taste	*superior collic* *rods & cones area 17*	c.	striate cortex — *vision*
b ___ voluntary movement		d.	spinal cord — *reflex*
e ___ olfaction		e.	limbic system — *olfaction*
	hair cells	f.	auditory cortex — *hearing*

B. Match the following to the modality that they represent or to any anatomical structure within the pathway known to mediate that modality.

_a_ superior colliculus		a.	rods and cones *Superior colliculus*
_d_ chorda tympani		b.	movement *Betys Cells*
_e_ smell		c.	hair cells *hearing*
_c_ hearing		d.	taste *Chorda tympani*
_b_ Betz cells		e.	mitral cells *Smell*

Short Answer

1. How does a complex nervous system operate to perceive the external environment?

2. Explain adaptation of a sensory receptor and discuss the advantage it offers an organism in its response to its external environment.

3. What mechanism allows spatial mapping of sensations?

4. What is believed to be the function of the superior colliculus? How does the sensory information it receives make this function possible?

5. What is a "grandmother" cell?

ANSWERS TO SELF-TEST

Multiple Choice

1. d	2. b	3. c	4. a	5. b	6. b	7. d
8. b	9. a	10. d	11. c	12. c	13. a	14. b
15. b						

True or False

1. T	2. F	3. T	4. F	5. T	6. T	7. F
8. F	9. F	10. T	11. F	12. F	13. T	14. F
15. T						

Matching

A.	1.	c	B	1.	a
	2.	f		2.	d
	3.	a		3.	e
	4.	b		4.	c
	5.	e		5.	b.

CHAPTER 5
HOMEOSTASIS

Before You Read This Chapter

OBJECTIVES

After reading this chapter, you should be able to do the following:

1. Know the components that make up the autonomic nervous system (ANS).

2. Understand the differences in structure and function between the sympathetic division and the parasympathetic division of the ANS.

3. The role of the diffuse enteric nervous system differs somewhat from the other aspects of the ANS. Be prepared to detail these differences.

4. The ANS is regulated primarily by two central nervous system components. You should know which brain regions are intimately associated with ANS function.

5. Be able to discuss the structure and function of the endocrine system.

6. Know the origins and targets of the hormones of the endocrine system?

7. Understand the operation of feedback control in regulating the activity of the endocrine system.

8. Be familiar with the concept of "set point."

9. Know the means of physiological regulation of temperature, blood volume and pressure, and appetite.

10. Understand the regulation of body weight and the factors thought to be responsible for this regulation.

OUTLINE

The autonomic nervous system

The sympathetic nervous system
The parasympathetic nervous system
Comparative features of the sympathetic and parasympathetic divisions
The diffuse enteric nervous system
Central regulation of the autonomic nervous system
    The hypothalamus
    The medulla oblongata

The endocrine system

The endocrine organs and their hormones
Concepts of endocrinology

Physiological set-points

Temperature regulation
Control of blood pressure and volume
Eating and eating behavior
    Appetite control: When to eat
    The set point hypothesis of eating
    Appetite control: When to stop eating
    Appetite control: Psychological factors
Eating disorders
    Anorexia and bulimia
    Obesity
Other set-point systems

Maintenance of the internal milieu

THEME

A large portion of the activity of the central nervous system is devoted to maintaining the internal environment of the body at constant levels. Proceeding largely outside the sphere of consciousness, this process is known as homeostasis. Homeostatic mechanisms control our body temperature, our food intake, our water and solid excretion rates, our blood glucose level, our blood pressure and volume, and a host of other physiological phenomena that we largely take for granted. In this chapter, we examine homeostasis and learn something about its physiological base. As is true with other brain systems, the goal of homeostatic regulation is to adapt the body's needs to the environment as both constantly change. This requires that the homeostatic systems have a means of detecting changes both in the environment and in the body in order to keep the internal environment constant.

A central theme in homeostasis is that of "adaptation." There are many kinds of adaptive responses that people make to changes in their environment. Some of them occur more or less automatically and are generally under the province of the ANS. Some students misread "autonomic nervous system" and in its place substitute "automatic nervous system." Although the name is incorrect this term more or less accurately describes the operation of the ANS, which operates, by and large, without any conscious control.

We adapt in many different ways to changes in our environment. Consider for a moment the kinds of adaptive responses that occur to cold. At one level of adaptation the ANS regulates our response by causing us to shiver and by routing blood away from the surface of the skin. On a higher level of adaptation, we will put on a jacket in order to protect ourselves from the winter's cold. On a still higher level of adaptation, we may move to a warmer climate, again to protect ourselves from the effects of cold. All these responses are properly considered examples of adaptive behavior. Only the first response, however, is under the direct and immediate control of the ANS. The last two examples--putting on a jacket and moving to Florida--represent a conscious effort that is removed from the considerations of homeostasis. Presumably, these last two forms of behavior represent exclusively human forms of adaptation. When animals grow a thick coat of fur to protect them from the winter, they do not do this under conscious control; for them, it is another manifestation of physiological adaptive mechanisms that do not involve consciousness.

Historically, the idea that the internal environment was an important aspect of body function and regulation was brought to the attention of the scientific world by the French physiologist Claude Bernard. This concept of the internal environment, or *milieu interne*, was expanded by the American physiologist Walter Cannon, who stressed the operation of homeostatic mechanisms that work to maintain a uniform internal environment.

When considering homeostasis, we should first direct our attention to the operation of ANS. The ANS possesses sensory components to monitor the internal environment and motor components to adjust physiological conditions to maintain appropriate homeostatic balance. ANS receptors detect the levels of body fluid, glucose in the bloodstream, and the temperature of the blood, to name only a few. The motor components of the ANS act to integrate the smooth muscles of the blood vessels and to integrate secretory gland activity.

Divisions of the ANS

The ANS is anatomically and functionally divided into two parts: the sympathetic and parasympathetic divisions. These two divisions differ anatomically both in the location of their components and in the neurotransmitters they utilize. One of the reasons that the ANS is considered separate from the central nervous system (CNS) is that it is located entirely in ganglia outside the CNS. In both the sympathetic and the parasympathetic ganglia, the CNS generally influences the ANS by means of the neurotransmitter acetylcholine. The synaptic transmitter that is utilized in the projection from the ganglia to the target tissue differs in the sympathetic and parasympathetic divisions. The sympathetic division, which arises primarily from the thoracic and lumbar portions of the spinal cord, utilizes the neurotransmitter norepinephrine. The parasympathetic division, which receives its CNS input from the brainstem and the sacral segments of the spinal cord, utilizes the neurotransmitter acetylcholine.

In most instances, the targets of the sympathetic and the parasympathetic divisions of the ANS are the same. For example, the cardiovascular system, composed of the heart and blood vessels, is influenced by both the sympathetic and parasympathetic divisions. This duality of innervation is a general rule for most organ systems.

Regulation of ANS Function

Generally, both the sympathetic and parasympathetic divisions of the ANS are active at the same time. What this means in terms of function is that the activity of the target tissue is a function of the relative balance of influence from the two divisions of the ANS. The sympathetic division has an activating or mobilizing effect on its targets, whereas the parasympathetic division has a "rest and recuperation" effect on the same targets. During moments of stress and arousal, the sympathetic division is dominant, whereas during periods of relaxation and reflection, the parasympathetic division is dominant. However, you should note that both divisions are continually active; only the relative difference between their influence changes.

For an example of the operation of these two divisions, consider what would happen if a grizzly bear were to walk into the room right now. Almost immediately, your sympathetic division would display increased activity and the parasympathetic division activity would decline. In terms of the effect of this change on your cardiovascular system, the sympathetic division would constrict smooth muscle fibers in the blood vessels, increasing blood pressure, and the parasympathetic division would decrease its activity, thus serving to speed up the heart and increase the force of heart contractions. Both of these effects would serve to enhance the ability of the blood to supply the muscles with oxygen in case you needed to fight or flee. Chapter 7, which deals with emotionality, will also consider the role of the ANS in our experience of emotion and the labeling of an event as "emotional." As will be discussed in that chapter, the perception of emotion depends both upon a reading of the internal state of the body and a conscious evaluation of the stressful stimulus.

Diffuse Enteric Nervous System

Another division of the ANS is the diffuse enteric nervous system. The diffuse enteric nervous system primarily innervates the glands and muscles of the gastrointestinal system. Like all muscles, the muscles of the stomach require neural impulses to initiate contraction (termed peristalsis) and are governed by the diffuse enteric nervous system. Our knowledge of the diffuse enteric nervous system is somewhat rudimentary, but it is known that acetylcholine is involved in the excitation of intestinal smooth muscle. It also seems probable that some of the local hormones that are involved in gastrointestinal activities are also capable of modulating the activities of other neurotransmitters.

The CNS modulates the activity of the ANS. Two regions of the brain that are most involved in regulating ANS functions are the hypothalamus and the medulla oblongata of the brainstem.

The Hypothalamus

If any one structure were to be singled out as the "center" of the brain, it would have to be the hypothalamus. The hypothalamus is the primary regulator of many visceral integrating functions. It consists of many individual nuclei that have specific jobs regulating a variety of aspects of homeostatic control. The hypothalamus and the pituitary gland work together quite closely to maintain homeostatic conditions. While the hypothalamus is generally considered to be "brain" and the pituitary is generally considered to be "gland," in reality the two tend to work together as a functional unit. For example, hypothalamic neurons regulate the secretion of hormones from the anterior lobe of the pituitary gland. In addition, the posterior lobe of the pituitary gland secretes hormones that are manufactured in the hypothalamus and shipped to the pituitary for release into the bloodstream.

The textbook delimits some of the functional divisions of the hypothalamus that are important to homeostatic activity. These divisions are the periventricular, the median, and the lateral zones of the hypothalamus. Cells in these regions are involved with homeostatic regulation, control of the endocrine system, and overriding input from higher brain structures, respectively. The medulla oblongata is involved in the control of respiration and heart rate. Interestingly, many of the organs innervated by components of the ANS are capable of functioning without any ANS influence at all. The heart of a frog will continue to beat when totally removed and placed in a dish of saline. Perhaps even more fascinating is that when the isolated frog heart is chopped into pieces, each of those pieces will continue to beat at its own rhythm. The ANS, however does serve to modulate and modify the activities of the organ that it innervates. A frog deprived of autonomic innervation of its heart would find itself unable to accelerate its heart rate to meet emergency demands and would be at a severe disadvantage when placed in a stressful situation.

Endocrine System

Another important part of the homeostatic system is the endocrine system. The body possesses two kinds of glands--exocrine and endocrine glands. Exocrine glands are often termed "ducted glands" because they secrete their product directly into a duct. The tear gland is an exocrine gland. An endocrine gland, in contrast, is termed a "ductless gland" because it secretes its product (a hormone) into the bloodstream. Since it is in the bloodstream, the hormone can potentially influence all cells in the body. The targets of an endocrine gland may thus be either widely distributed throughout the body or in specific locations. For example, growth hormones affect a majority of the cells of the body, whereas gonadal hormones have specific target cells primarily located in the gonadal organs.

Just as neurotransmitters bind to receptors located in the synapse of recipient cells, hormones bind to receptors located on or in their target cells. A further parallel between the brain and the endocrine system is that some of the endocrine hormones also act on brain cells by virtue of the fact that neurons possess receptors for those hormones. As an aside, it is important to understand that the distinctions that we make between various systems within the body are often arbitrary and can fail to take into consideration their integrated operation. For example, the distinction that is often made between gland and brain may not be particularly useful, since the two systems interact quite extensively.

There are numerous glands that make up the endocrine system, all of which are discussed in some detail in the text, along with the hormones that they secrete, their target cells, and the actions that these hormones have on the target tissue. It is important to recognize that the pituitary gland is intimately linked with the hypothalamus and that the two structures operate in an integrated manner. Some of the hormones that are released from the pituitary originate in the hypothalamus, and others that originate in the pituitary are released under hypothalamic neural control. The textbook details the means by which the hypothalamus and pituitary interact. Together, the hypothalamus and pituitary represent one of the control centers for homeostatic regulation and exert neuroendocrine control over bodily needs.

One aspect of hormonal secretion that deserves some discussion is the regulation of hormonal concentration in the bloodstream and thus in the target tissue is regulated. Hormones are very potent chemicals, and only very small amounts are needed to activate the target tissue. It is necessary to control precisely the amount of hormones circulating in the blood. To achieve a high degree of control over hormonal secretion, the principles of "feedback" extensively govern neuroendocrine function. To take one example, consider the release of luteinizing hormone (LH) and follicle-stimulating hormone (FSH) from the anterior lobe of the pituitary. These hormones are released upon receipt of hypophysiotropic hormone (through the pituitary portal blood supply) from the preoptic area of the hypothalamus. Once LH and FSH are in the bloodstream, the target cells in the gonads are activated. Upon activation, the gonads produce primarily estrogen or testosterone, depending upon the sex of the individual. As is discussed in Chapter 6, Rhythms of the Brain, the level of estrogen in the bloodstream varies according to the estrous or menstrual cycle. The estrogen that is produced by the female gonads is secreted into the blood supply and in turn regulates the amount of hypophysiotropic hormone, which then regulates the production of FSH and LH in the anterior pituitary. Since the feedback signal (estrogen) "turns off" the system, it is termed "negative feedback." Other examples of negative feedback occur in many different aspects of the neuroendocrine control system.

Physiological Set-Point

One of the first things that most people do when they become ill is to take their temperature. The body temperature of a human is normally 98.6 degrees Fahrenheit. Any deviation from normality is usually a sign of a dysfunction in the body, such as an infection. Therefore, any variation in body temperature is an important clue to a physician that a disease process is occurring. How can the body be capable of regulating its own internal temperature with such precision (maintaining the 98.6 F "set point"), given the wide fluctuation in ambient temperatures to which we are all exposed? An analogy to the thermostat that operates in your home or apartment may help to clarify the role of set point. When you set your home thermostat at 70 degrees, sensors in the thermostat detect the temperature in the room and turn on the furnace if the temperature falls below 70 degrees and turn it off when the temperature rises above 70 degrees. The same process occurs in bodily homeostatic systems, in which internal sensors detect the temperature of the blood and any variation from the set point temperature brings into play mechanisms designed to bring the temperature back to its set point.

There are many examples of the operation of set-point regulatory mechanisms in the body, and they include the control of such phenomena as temperature, blood glucose, salt, and oxygen. The textbook describes the means by which both internal temperature receptors in the hypothalamus (which sense the internal temperature) and external temperature receptors on the surface of the skin (which represent the air temperature) work together to maintain body temperature at the set-point value. If the body temperature drops, the ANS works to increase metabolism, to shunt blood away from the skin, and to create "goosebumps." Similarly, if the hypothalamic detectors register an increase in blood temperature, heat-reduction mechanisms are activated. Given the body's efforts to maintain the set point, you may wonder why an infection results in an elevated temperature. The elevated body temperature may help to destroy invading bacteria, which cannot survive at higher temperatures. This is not the whole story, however. Some scientists suspect that bacterial toxins have the ability to alter the set-point value itself. The textbook contains discussions of the operation of set point for other physiologically controlled variables, such as the operation of the cardiovascular system and the maintenance of appropriate fluid levels in the body. All of these control processes feature sensory detectors used to compare the actual event with the set point and motor mechanisms that can be called into play to alter the system to restore the desired set point.

Some physiological variables are only partially controlled by the ANS. The eating behavior of humans, for example, is partially under the control of the ANS and other regulatory systems, and partly under the control of learning and social factors. We sometimes eat, not because we are hungry but because we are with others in a setting in which one traditionally eats. In the case of eating, the system is multiply controlled, in part by ANS mechanisms and in large part by higher cognitive processes.

Metabolic energy and material is ultimately derived from the food eaten. Glucose, fats, amino acids, and carbohydrates are molecules necessary for life. Glucose, in the body, requires insulin as a pre-requisite for cellular uptake and use. This is not the case in the brain--where glucose can be utilized without insulin (although insulin appears to act in brain to modulate eating). Adiposity (stored fat) is a major regulatory factor in eating. Adipocytes (fat cells) are larger and more numerous in the obese, and appear to secrete a factor(s) important in regulating the eating set-point. Some of the blood-born factors have been tentatively identified, and include cholecystokinin (a gut peptide), lipoprotein lipase (an enzyme important in regulating body fat), norepinephrine (a neurotransmitter), and the endorphins (a family of neuropeptides).

Homeostasis

Homeostasis is the process by which the internal environment of the body maintains equilibrium in the face of fluctuating external conditions and internal requirements. We have seen that the body employs both the ANS and the endocrine system in accomplishing the goals of homeostasis. The ANS is composed of two opposing divisions, the sympathetic division and the parasympathetic division. Virtually all organs are innervated by both divisions of the ANS, and the relative balance of activity between the two divisions determines the effect on the target tissue. The sympathetic division of the ANS is primarily concerned with arousal and reaction, and the parasympathetic division is primarily concerned with rest and rehabilitation.

The endocrine system, which is more appropriately termed the neuroendocrine system because of the integrated activity among the hypothalamus, pituitary, and other endocrine glands, is the other major component of homeostatic regulation. The hypothalamus regulates a variety of functions through its effects on the pituitary gland and on pituitary hormone secretion. Further, the hormones produced by the target tissue feed back to the hypothalamus, which regulates the level of pituitary output. The operation of both the ANS and the endocrine system features feedback control and the utilization of set points as targets for homeostatic regulation. All the aforementioned phenomena do not occur in isolation; rather, all the homeostatic regulation by the brain is done in a highly coordinated manner. It would not do to have one part of the brain deciding it was time to eat, while another part of the brain was mobilizing the musculature for action. The means by which this information is integrated and controlled depends in part upon the activity of the neuroendocrine system and in part upon influences imposed from higher brain centers. All these behaviors are also controlled in part by circadian rhythms, which are discussed in Chapter 6.

QUESTIONS TO KEEP IN MIND AS YOU READ THIS CHAPTER

1.   By what means does the body maintain constant internal conditions in the face of changing environmental factors?

2. What would life would be like if we had to devote considerable conscious effort to maintaining body temperature, blood glucose, and fluid levels rather than relying on an automatic system to regulate these variables?

3. The behavior of many animals is more rigidly controlled by endocrine hormones than is the case for human beings--for whom social factors are also important. What adaptive advantage might have led to this difference?

4. What is the role of the hypothalamus in regulating ANS action?

5. How do hormones work, and how is their activity regulated by the neuroendocrine system?

6. "Feedback" control and "set point" are important concepts in neuroendocrine control. How do they work?

7. Temperature regulation can be accomplished on many different levels. Which brain structures are involved in these different modes of adaptive response?

After You Have Read the Chapter, Continue with the Following Material

STUDENT'S OUTLINE

After you read this chapter and study the material it contains, close the book and in the space below, using your own words, try to outline the major points that you have just read. The basic structure of the chapter is provided below.

The autonomic nervous system

The endocrine system

Physiological set-points

Maintenance of the internal milieu

Now that you have attempted to outline this chapter from memory, go back to the textbook and see how accurate your recollection was. Fill in those topics you might have missed and emphasize the points that are stressed in the textbook.

Key Terms

The following terms were introduced in this chapter. Be sure that you know these terms and can define them.

Adipocyte
Adiposity
Adrenal cortex
Adrenal medulla
Angiotensin II
Angiotensinogen
Anorexia nervosa
Autonomic nervous system
Brown adipose tissue
Bulimia
Cholecystokinin
Cortisol
Endocrine organ
Exocrine gland
Follicle-stimulating hormone (FSH)
Ganglia
Gland
Homeostasis
Hormones
Hypophysiotropic hormone
Hypothalamus
Islet cells of the pancreas
Juxtaglomerular cell
Lipoprotein lipase (LPL)
Luteinizing hormone
Oxytocin
Parasympathetic nervous system
Parathyroid
Peristalsis
Pituitary gland
Pituitary-portal circulation
Postganglionic fibers
Preganglionic fibers
Renin
Sacral segments
Satiety factors
Somatostatin
Sympathetic nervous system
Thyroid
Vagus nerve
Vasopressin

Multiple Choice

1. Which of the following is an endocrine structure?
   a. periventricular zone
   b. sympathetic ganglia
   c. nucleus of the solitary tract
   d. adrenal medulla

2. Which of the following similarities between the CNS and the endocrine system IS INCORRECT?
   a. norepinephrine, somatostatin, vasopressin and oxytocin are used in both systems.
   b. both systems involve secretion of a "chemical message"
   c. the onset and time-course of action are similar in both systems
   d. cholecystokinin and vasoactive intestinal polypeptide are used in both systems

3. The periventricular area of the hypothalamus is not involved in
   a. releasing corticotropin-releasing factor
   b. body temperature adjustment
   c. regulating medial zone hormone release
   d. releasing somatostatin

4. Which of the following neurotransmitters is implicated in the central control of eating?
   a. acetylcholine
   b. dopamine
   c. norepinephrine
   d. substance P

5. Which of the following is NOT associated with anorexia nervosa?
   a. loss of appetite
   b. significant weight loss
   c. some anorectics engage in bulimia
   d. the anorectic is concerned about being too thin

6. An animal just underwent an experiment involving surgical removal of a neural subsystem but, unless stressed, seems to be unaffected by it. Which part of this animal was probably involved?
   a. parasympathetic nervous system
   b. sympathetic nervous system
   c. enteric nervous system
   d. hypothalamus

7. Which of the following is not a function of the vagus nerve?
   a. inhibits heart, lung, and intestinal actions
   b. delivers norepinephrine as a neurotransmitter
   c. responds to cholecystokinin in some of its sensory components
   d. carries incoming sensory information back to preganglionic levels

8. The regulatory functions of the hypothalamus include
   a. reproductive cycle preparation
   b. regulation of skeletal muscle reflexes
   c. vasopressin secretion
   d. blood pressure regulation

9. The autonomic nervous system and the endocrine system both
   a. have acetylcholine-containing neurons in the spinal cord
   b. depend on cortical input to function
   c. utilize feedback control to regulate their activity
   d. involve balancing of opposing units or functions e.g., agonist-antagonist muscle pairs

10. Which of the following factors has been implicated as playing an important role in human obesity?
    a. an efficient metabolism
    b. increased lipoprotein lipase levels
    c. increased adipocyte volume
    d. all the above

11. The hypothalamus is implicated in each of the following except
    a. vasopressin and oxytocin secretion
    b. regulation of the anterior lobe of the pituitary
    c. spontaneous respiratory movements, blood pressure, and cardiovascular rhythm adjustments
    d. fluid, salt, and nutrient concentration, temperature balance

12. It has been said that humans can function relatively independently of the changing physical demands of the world; the part of the hypothalamus that suggests this description is the
    a. paraventricular zone
    b. ventral medial nucleus
    c. medial zone
    d. lateral zone

13. Identify the mismatched pair
    a. preganglionic: acetylcholine
    b. postganglionic sympathetic: norepinephrine
    c. adrenal medulla: dopamine
    d. postganglionic parasympathetic: acetylcholine

14. Which of the following may not be directly affected by a disruption of the reticular formation such as an infection?
    a. attention
    b. respiratory movements
    c. body temperature
    d. feeding

15. All of the following are receptor areas related to blood volume or blood pressure homeostasis except
    a. atrial stretch receptors
    b. cardiac arch receptors
    c. periventricular neurons
    d. baroreceptors

True or False

_____ 1. The pituitary portal circulation carries hormones into the posterior lobe of the pituitary.

_____ 2. The effect of hypothalamic influences on the anterior lobe of the pituitary is to trigger the release of hormones that travel to specific target cells.

_____ 3. Regulation of blood pressure and volume requires both hormonal and neurotransmitter-related mechanisms.

_____ 4. All other things being equal, destruction of juxtaglomerular cells will reduce drinking behavior.

_____ 5. In a critically wounded and bleeding patient, one would expect to find high levels of angiotensin II.

_____ 6. Hypothalamic neurons secrete their hypophysiotropic hormones into the pituitary-portal circulation where they travel to targets throughout the body.

_____ 7. The observation that people tend to becone somewhat overweight past the age of 40 suggests that the set-point for body weight is can change on a long-term basis.

_____ 8. Experiments with animals has shown that overfeeding in infancy has no effect on adult body weight.

_____ 9. Obese human are not very discriminating in what they consume, eating large quantities of doubtful-tasting food.

_____ 10. A simple way to recall the actions of the parasympathetic nervous system is to reconstruct what happens when an animal must mobilize for "fight or flight."

_____ 11. All acetylcholine transmitters activate an identical type of receptor.

_____ 12. Nerves from thoracic spinal segments give rise to the vagus nerve, which supplies all the parasympathetic innervation of the heart and lungs.

_____ 13. There is no basis to support any animal model of integration of human visceral function in the hypothalamus.

_____ 14. The genital organs are dually innervated by both the parasympathetic and sympathetic nervous systems.

_____ 15. The atrium of the heart possesses detectors for blood volume condition and hormones to induce salt loss in the kidney.

Matching

___g___ 1. hypothalamus

___f___ 2. vagus nerve

___e___ 3. baroreceptors

___i___ 4. short preganglionic fibers

___j___ 5. enteric nervous system

___h___ 6. medial hypothalamus

___c___ 7. lateral hypothalamus

___a___ 8. lumbar and thoracic autonomic nerves

___d___ 9. cranial and sacral autonomic nerves

___b___ 10. periventricular zone

a. fight and flight

b. supervises medial zone

c. integrates cortical and environmental information

d. rest and recuperation

e. average blood pressure

f. cholecystokinin

g. the master gland

h. secretes hormones

i. sympathetic nervous system

j. peristalsis

Short Answer

1. Why is the pituitary no longer regarded as the master gland?

2. Name two differences between neurotransmitters and hormones.

3. What experiment supports the idea that both the parasympathetic and the sympathetic nervous systems have to be active simultaneously for an organism to respond adaptively?

4. What is the property of set-point systems that makes them a useful description for endocrine function?

5. What is homeostasis and why is it necessary for human functioning?

ANSWERS TO SELF-TEST

Multiple Choice

1.	d	2.	c	3.	a	4.	c	5.	d	6.	b	7.	b
8.	a	9.	c	10.	d	11.	c	12.	d	13.	c	14.	c
15.	c												

True or False

1.	F	2.	T	3.	T	4.	T	5.	T	6.	F	7.	T
8.	F	9.	F	10.	F	11.	F	12.	F	13.	F	14.	T
15.	T												

Matching

1. g
2. f
3. e
4. i
5. j
6. h
7. c
8. a
9. d
10. b

CHAPTER 6
RHYTHMS OF THE BRAIN

Before You Read This Chapter

OBJECTIVES

After reading this chapter, you should be able to do the following:

1. Realize that circadian rhythms occur in virtually all organisms, from single-celled plants to human beings.

2. Know that the three major patterns of biological rhythms are termed circadian, infradian, and ultradian rhythms.

3. Understand that many forms of rhythmic behavior occur on long time scale and are triggered by some aspect in the environment.

4. Realize that the most important environmental cues for controlling rhythmic behavior appear to be light and temperature.

5. Be aware that human circadian rhythms are tied to the 24-hour day but are actually longer when allowed to "free run."

6. Know that the best candidate for the master rhythmic brain center appears to be the suprachiasmatic nucleus of the hypothalamus.

7. Be familiar with the brain activity known as rapid eye movement (REM) sleep. During sleep, dream periods occur at approximately 90-minute intervals.

8. Understand that the reproductive cycle represents a powerful biological rhythm that is driven by the secretion of hormones from the hypothalamus and pituitary.

9. Be aware of the idea that disorders of the brain's rhythms may underlie some mental illnesses, particularly those that manifest as seasonal rhythmic depression.

10. The basic characteristics of biological clocks, the brain circuitry, the environmental cues necessary and the adaptive significance of the biological rhythm should be understood.

OUTLINE

Types of rhythms

Studies of rhythms in nonhuman organisms

    Simple organisms
    Birds and mammals
    The role of environmental cues
    The pineal gland
        Input pathways
        Pacemaking activities

Human circadian rhythms

    Sleep/wakefulness
    When rhythms fall out of place
        Jet lag
        Shift work

Human ultradian rhythms

    Sleep cycles
    REM sleep

Human infradian rhythms

    The human female reproductive cycle
    Seasonal rhythms

Sexual behavior: Rhythms and cycles

    Lordosis in female rats
    Hormones and sexual behavior
    Human sexual behavior
        Of mice and men
        Sex and the cerebral cortex
        Homosexuality
        Human sexual response

Pacemakers in the mammalian brain: The suprachiasmatic nuclei

Multiple pacemakers

Rhythms and psychological disturbance

    Depression
    Delayed sleep-phase insomnia

Characteristics of biological clocks

THEME

As much as some of us would like to deny it, we are creatures of habit. This means simply that humans and other animals behave in relatively predictable ways in terms of many of the basic biological rhythms that pervade their lives. Humans and other animals tend to behave in a rhythmic fashion with respect to sleeping, eating, mating, migration, hibernation, and a host of other activities. In most cases, the biological underpinnings and environmental triggers for these rhythmic behaviors and physiological processes are incompletely understood. In some cases we cannot even appreciate the reason for the behavior in the first place, much less understand its mechanism of control. For example, we cannot answer the question of what is the nature and function of sleep. We do know that if an animal or a person is deprived of sleep, behavioral disturbances will result, but we do not know the biological or psychological function of sleep.

Many rhythms of the brain are not readily apparent to the casual observer. We are not routinely aware of, nor do we monitor, changes in the concentration of hormones in the bloodstream. Similarly, alterations in our sleep cycles that may interfere with the amount of dreaming may not be readily apparent. What is true of both of these examples, however, is that there may be certain behavioral manifestations of the disruption of these biological rhythms. Evidence is accumulating that for some individuals, disruptions in biological rhythms may be the root of some medical complaints, such as seasonal depression.

Types of Rhythms

Research into simple unicellular organisms and complex multicellular animals has indicated that there are several types of rhythms. Rhythms that have a periodicity of approximately 24 hours are termed circadian rhythms. Biological rhythms that occur over a period of time longer than a day are termed infradian rhythms, and rhythms that repeat more than once a day are called ultradian rhythms. In all cases these rhythms are best studied when the organism is removed from environmental cues, so that one can be sure that the rhythm is intrinsic to the brain and that the behavior or physiological response is not simply occurring in response to an environmental stimulus. These experiments are conducted by placing organisms into an environment in which they are isolated from all environmental cues that might signal time of day or season of the year. Research into brain rhythms has several goals: to discover (1) how a rhythm is organized, (2) where the pacemaker that drives the rhythm is located and how it operates, and (3) which biological mechanisms cause the pacemaker to generate the rhythm.

Isolation Experiments

Isolation experiments have demonstrated that a wide spectrum of species continue to display rhythms in the absence of environmental cues and thus these can be considered truly endogenous rhythms. It is important to realize that although circadian rhythms do function in the absence of environmental cues such as light or temperature, the environmental cues often serve to synchronize the inherent biological rhythm. These observations indicate that circadian and other rhythms are not dependent upon either a brain or cues from the environment for their organization. Clearly, plants and unicellular animals can display biological rhythms in the total absence of a central nervous system. Thus, the underlying mechanism of biological rhythms is something that is not unique to the nervous system. In human beings, such biological rhythms have been studied by employing the isolation experiment as well. In one dramatic example of such an isolation experiment a subject lived for long periods of time in deep caves that were totally closed off from normal environmental cues. In this instance, the subject was entirely freed from time-giving cues and their rhythms were said to be "free running." In the absence of environmental cues, the human sleep-waking cycle initially becomes quite erratic, but later stabilizes at a cycle that is somewhat longer than the 24-hour day.

Infradian rhythms also display their periodicity in the absence of environmental cues, as studies of both migration and hibernation indicate. The adaptive significance of an organism's possessing an internal biological clock that is all but impervious to environmental cues can be seen in the example of a hibernating squirrel. If the animal's hibernation were totally controlled by environmental triggers, such as a decline in temperature, an animal experiencing a prolonged warm spell in the fall might fail to build up fat stores and food supplies for the winter and be caught unprepared by the sudden arrival of winter.

An example that is not discussed in the text might further clarify the difference between purely rhythmic behavior and triggered rhythmicity. Some animals such as the rabbit are known as reflex ovulators. In such an estrous cycle the female periodically comes into heat, during which time she is receptive to the mating advances of males. An animal living in the wild, however, may encounter a male at times other than when the reproductive system is ready for fertilization. In the case of the rabbit, when mating occurs at non-optimal times during the estrous cycle because of the fortuitous encounter with an amorous male, the female rabbit responds by reflexively ovulating so that the mating may lead to fertilization.

Some environmental cues can influence organisms' internal rhythmic states; the most important appear to be time and light cues. The lengthening days of the spring may trigger reproductive behaviors, while the shortening days in the fall may trigger the fat deposition and food hoarding common in many animals in preparation for hibernation and alterations in temperature.

Pineal Gland

In some species, there is an environmental cuing of light-driven biological rhythms. In some species the pineal gland (located inside the brain) it receives neural input from the visual system, whereas in other species, such as birds, it is capable of sensing light directly through the skull. Interestingly, pineal glands that are removed from birds and kept in cultures respond to changes in lighting conditions, showing that they possess light receptors that are sensitive to alterations in environmental illumination.

The pineal gland acts as a pacemaker for other regions of the brain and body through the transformation of the neurotransmitter serotonin into the hormone melatonin by means of the enzyme N-acetyl-transferase. Like all enzymes, N-acetyltransferase facilitates chemical reactions. The amounts of circulating melatonin vary according to the amount of N-acetyltransferase and to the variation in light illumination affecting the pineal gland.

The mechanism of action of the pineal gland has been well studied in the chicken. (As an aside, the common chicken has been the subject of a variety of fundamental scientific studies. In addition to helping to describe the role of the pineal gland in circadian behavior, the chicken has been instrumental in understanding the nature of social hierarchies among animals, better known as the pecking order. Part of the reason for this interest in the chicken stems from its economic importance.) The morning light that reaches the pineal gland of the chicken reduces the activity of N-acetyl-transferase. This, in turn, reduces the amount of melatonin circulating in the chicken's blood plasma, and as a consequence there is an increase in the body temperature and a change in the behavior of the bird. While the mechanism of sleep-wakefulness is partially understood in the chicken, it has not been possible to extend these observations to humans or even to laboratory rats, because their governing mechanisms appear to be quite different.

Pacemakers

Although it is common to consider sleep and wakefulness as the only circadian rhythms of any importance, in fact there are over a hundred such biological rhythms in humans. Such physiological phenomena as body temperature, blood glucose levels, urine flow, hormone levels and many other physiological and behavioral states vary according to day-night cycles. It is of the greatest importance to recognize that all these rhythms are in synchrony with the sleep-waking cycle of the body. This observation suggests that there might be a master pacemaker in the brain which then synchronizes all the other pacemakers into synchronous activity. The experiments done in caves indicate that while sleep and wakefulness may run free at one frequency, other physiological variables, such as body temperature, may be quite out of harmony with the sleep-wakefulness cycle. Normally, however, environmental cues serve to synchronize and trigger all these cycles together.

The best candidate for the job of master coordinator of all the other pacemakers is the suprachiasmatic nucleus of the hypothalamus. If the suprachiasmatic nucleus is damaged or otherwise inactivated, many of the rhythms of the body lose their synchrony and begin to run free. This observation suggests that one of the functions of the suprachiasmatic nucleus is to coordinate and synchronize the other pacemakers of the brain.

Sleep

As we mentioned earlier, the function of sleep is not known. It is certainly a biological requirement for humans, but we do not completely understand the biological necessity for sleep. Something is known, however, of the brain mechanisms that appear to control sleep and wakefulness. The reticular formation of the brainstem and the midbrain has been found to be involved in arousal and attentive alertness patterns. Nuclei located in the upper brainstem are implicated in controlling sleep and dreaming. The raphe nuclei induce sleep by inhibiting the activity of the reticular formation through the release of the neurotransmitter serotonin. Serotonin depletion results in insomnia in laboratory animals. The second brain stem structure implicated in sleep and dreaming is the locus coeruleus, which is the main site for norepinephrine-containing neurons. The interaction of these three structures, the reticular formation, the raphe nuclei, and the locus coeruleus, results in periods of sleep, dreaming, and wakefulness.

Disruptions of Biological Rhythms

The effective disruption of the normal rhythms of the brain can be quite debilitating. Cave dwellers initially noted a period of disorientation until they established a new rhythm after they were in the cave for some period of time. On a more familiar level, studies of workers whose jobs require that they rotate shifts show that the periodic shifting of a worker from the graveyard shift to the swing shift and day shift is quite disruptive, both for the worker and for productivity in the work place.

Jet lag may be familiar to you if you have taken an airplane trip that crosses several time zones in a short period of time. Like shift changing, jet lag is a desynchronization of the internal body-brain rhythms from the environmental cues around us. Scientists have termed these desynchronizations "phase shifts." Some phase shifts are more difficult to adjust to than others. It has long been appreciated that it is more difficult to adjust to an eastbound flight than to an equivalent westbound flight. In an westbound flight the biological clock looses time relative to the 24-hour day; to catch up, rhythms must phase-delay. Phase-delay is evidently easier for the body to adjust to than phase-advance, which occurs after eastbound flights.

Ultradian Rhythms

Humans display several important ultradian rhythms. One of the most fascinating of these is the occurrence of dream activity at roughly 90-minute intervals throughout the sleep cycle. The brain shows regular changes in electroencephalographic (EEG) activity as one enters into sleep and dream states. The changes in electroencephalographic activity have been categorized in a number of different ways. The textbook discusses one way of describing the EEG changes associated with sleep dreaming. At a certain stage in the progression of EEG waves, a pattern of activity is shown that is very similar to that seen during alert wakefulness. During this EEG stage of sleep, if an individual is awakened, he or she will almost invariably report the occurrence of a dream; if an individual is awakened during one of the other EEG stages of sleep, dreams are rarely reported. Therefore this stage of EEG sleep appears to be correlated with the presence of dreaming. Since during a dream the eyes move rapidly beneath the eyelids, the name rapid eye movement (REM) sleep has been given to this stage.

The brain involvement during sleep and dream sleep indicates that there are periodic interactions between the locus coeruleus and the reticular formation that are correlated with the occurrence of dream sleep. As we stated earlier, the function of sleep is not known, and it should not come as a surprise that the function of dreaming is also unknown. Interestingly, all mammals appear to display REM sleep.

Reproductive Rhythms

The human female reproductive cycle, sometimes termed the menstrual cycle, offers a well-known example of a human infradian rhythm. Although human sexual behavior is little influenced by infradian hormonal rhythms and is governed more by societal and learned experiences, the reproductive and mating behaviors of many nonhuman animals are quite rigidly controlled by cyclic variations in hormone levels. In humans these hormonal cues have been almost completely overridden by societal and learned cues. Physiologically, in our endocrine system the hypothalamus initiates the beginning of each reproductive cycle by secreting gonadotropin-releasing hormone (GRH) into the anterior pituitary, where it stimulates the production and release of follicle-stimulating hormone (FSH) and luteinizing hormone (LH) at appropriate times. The textbook discusses the action of FSH and LH on the ovary to stimulate the growth of the follicle that contains the ovum. As the follicle grows, it secretes estrogen into the blood stream; the estrogen feeds back to the pituitary, inhibiting the release of FSH. Estrogen also stimulates the release of LH, which causes the mature ovum to be released. The remaining follicle becomes a secreting gland known as the corpus luteum. The corpus luteum secretes the hormone progesterone, which prepares the uterine wall for implantation of a fertilized egg. Experiments with laboratory animals have shown that environmental cues can influence the reproductive cycle of female animals, as would be expected in this brain-derived rhythm.

Rhythms and Psychological Disturbances

It has only been recently appreciated that humans are influenced by seasonal rhythms in a manner possibly analogous to the way in which animals are influenced by these rhythms in terms of migration and hibernation. While humans have not been known to hibernate, there are many reports of seasonal changes in mood that may be tied to environmental cues. It is not uncommon to encounter individuals who have become depressed in the depths of winter and who are correspondingly elated and energetic in the middle of summer. It is not inconceivable that the human pineal gland or other brain structures may be responsible for these mood changes. It will be interesting to observe the effect of manipulating environmental cues on these afflicted patients to see if their mood swings can be altered by changing the environmental illumination. Other experiments reported in the text discuss some promising treatments of other forms of behavior disorders based upon the notion that the underlying cause of the mental disturbance might be related to disruptions of rhythms of the brain. These treatments, while only in their infancy, may hold the promise of alleviating some severe disturbances of mental and emotional function if we can utilize these rhythmic systems to control behavior.

Our current knowledge of biological rhythms suggests that there exist multiple pacemakers located in the brain and elsewhere that are synchronized by a master pacemaker, probably the suprachiasmatic nucleus in mammals, and that are triggered by environmental cues. There is growing evidence that when the biological rhythms become desynchronized, either due to changes in the environment or due to unknown processes occuring in the brain, unpleasant and undesirable consequences may result. You might reflect on the adaptive significance of these biological rhythms. All biological rhythms appear to be genetically programmed and are products of a lengthy evolutionary process. The control of biological rhythms is flexible, however, allowing organisms to respond to cues in their environments to optimize the adaptive change they can make to those environments.

Characteristics of Biological Clocks

In this chapter we have reviewed most of the rhythms of the brain. We have seen that there are three kinds of rhythms, all of which are ultimately linked to the day-night rhythm of the environment. They have different periodicities: Rhythms that occur on approximately a 24-hour cycle are termed circadian rhythms; those that occur over a longer period are infradian; and those that occur more than once during the 24-hour day are termed ultradian. The goal of this chapter has been to investigate how these rhythms are organized and which behavior patterns they influence, and to learn where the brain pacemakers are located that control these rhythms and to what environmental influences they respond. Ultimately, it is our goal to understand the cellular mechanisms that cause the pacemakers to generate these rhythms and how these pacemakers influence other regions of the brain.

We should remember that these rhythmic alterations in biological function are not limited to the central nervous system. Studies have shown that unicellular organisms and plants also display biological rhythms, which clearly indicates that a nervous system is not necessary for these specific rhythms to occur.

We have seen that the biological rhythms are inherent in the organism, since when the organism is isolated from the environment the rhythms persist, although they may do so at a different rate of time. Environmental cues or events can serve to synchronize or trigger the biological rhythm. The two prime environmental cues are light period and temperature.

There are a number of brain pacemakers that are involved in regulating these rhythmic changes. The pineal gland, through the action of the enzyme N-acetyltransferase, serves to convert the neurotransmitter serotonin into melatonin, which then causes temperature and motor activity in some species. The pineal gland is sensitive to changes in illumination and governs the chemical machinery through its interaction with light energy. Other brain regions are involved in different aspects of rhythmic behaviors. The hypothalamus secretes

81

GRH, which influences the human female reproductive cycle via two other hormones, FSH and LH. Still other brain regions are involved in the regulation of sleep, dreaming and wakefulness. These structures are brainstem nuclei and consist of the reticular formation, the raphe nuclei and the locus coeruleus.

The search for the master pacemaker in the brain that coordinates all the other pacemakers centers upon a nucleus in the hypothalamus-- the suprachiasmatic nucleus. This structure, when removed from the brain, continues to cycle in the absence of environmental input, and the other biological rhythms in the body then appear to free run when they are not being influenced by the suprachiasmatic nucleus.

There are numerous kinds of human biological rhythms, ranging from the circadian rhythms of body temperature, sleep and wakefulness to the ultradian rhythms of dream periods and sleep cycles. Human infradian rhythms include phenomena such as the female reproductive cycle and perhaps the seasonal rhythmic depression.

The effect on individuals of disrupting biological rhythms can be quite severe. When rhythms fall out of phase, either because of imposed isolation or because of as yet unknown brain dysfunctions, the results can be quite serious. Considerable interest is being shown in the consequences of disruption of biological rhythms that may lead to forms of insomnia and mental illness. Less serious disruption of biological rhythms is seen in the commonly experienced jet lag, which is caused by phase shifting of the biological rhythm with respect to the 24-hour day; a similar phenomenon is observed when workers are required to change or rotate shifts periodically. Both these phenomena have effects on mood and ability as well as on performance. As we understand more and more about the biological rhythms of the body and brain, we can begin to adjust our lives to minimize the impact of desynchronization on human performance.

Rhythms of the brain do not occur in isolation; they are quite capable of influencing many spheres of everyday life. Minor forms of biological rhythm desynchronization can markedly impair an individual's performance and will reduce his or her quality of life. As you proceed through this course, do not view these biological rhythms in isolation but consider the impact that they will have on other forms of brain-controlled activity such as emotionality, motivation, learning, memory and the like.

QUESTIONS TO KEEP IN MIND AS YOU READ THIS CHAPTER

1. What are the various kinds of biological rhythms that have been identified?

2. How do biological rhythms differ among plants, single-celled animals, and complicated multicellular organisms such as humans?

3. What is the adaptive significance of a biological rhythm controlling reproductive behavior?

4. What is known of the brain mechanisms that control biological rhythms and to what environmental stimuli do they appear to respond?

5. Reflect on your own life and see if you can identify any disturbances in your own biological rhythms. Note any consequences of such a disturbance to your emotional, physiological, or intellectual activities.

6. We live in an environment that has changed radically in the last one hundred years. This is not the environment that has existed for most of the long period of our evolution. Consider what effects this "new" environment might have on brain systems that have evolved to deal with a different set of circumstances.

7. The biological necessity for sleep and dreaming is unknown. What are some possible biological functions that might be served by sleep and dreaming, and how might you test these ideas to see if they are valid?

8. It is widely observed that many mammals as well as human infants exhibit REM sleep and are probably dreaming. What do you imagine the content of these dreams to be?

STUDENT'S OUTLINE

After you have read this chapter and studied the material that it contains, close the book and in the space below, using your own words, try to outline the major points of what you have just read. The basic structure of the chapter is provided below.

Types of rhythms

Studies of rhythms in nonhuman organisms

Human circadian rhythms

Human ultradian rhythms

Human infradian rhythms

Sexual behavior: Rhythms and cycles

Pacemakers in the mammalian brain:

Multiple pacemakers

Rhythms and psychological disturbance

Characteristics of biological clocks

Now that you have attempted to outline this chapter from memory, go back to the textbook and see how accurate your recollection was. Fill in those topics that you might have missed and emphasize the points that are stressed in the textbook.

Key Terms

The following terms were introduced in this chapter. You should be sure that these terms are familiar to you and that you have their definitions well in hand.

Circadian rhythms
Corpus luteum
Desynchronization
Estrogen
Gonad
Gonadrotorpin-releasing hormone (GRH)
Infradian rhythm
Lordosis
Melatonin
N-acetyltransferase

Ovulation
Ovum
Phase-advance
Phase-delay
Phase shift
Pineal gland
Progesterone
Rapid eye movement (REM) sleep
Reticular formation
Suprachiasmatic nuclei
Ultradian rhythm
Zeitgeber

SELF-TEST

Multiple Choice

1. The human circadian rhythm of sleep-wakefulness in outer space
   a. synchronizes to the orbital cycle of the spacecraft
   b. deteriorates and becomes arrhythmic
   c. is stabilized by forcing the astronauts to stick to a planned schedule
   d. remains linked to earth rhythms

2. A characteristic of the mammalian reproductive system of males is
   a. negative feedback
   b. independence from the circadian rhythm system
   c. ultradian rhythm
   d. control by the pineal gland

3. A feature of human depressive illness is
   a. absence of REM sleep
   b. excess of REM sleep
   c. seasonal variation
   d. noncyclic nature

4. The beginning of the reproductive cycle is triggered by which structure
   a. pineal gland
   b. pituitary
   c. ovary
   d. hypothalamus

5. There exist at least two clusters of biological rhythms in humans. One cluster includes the rhythm of sleep/wakefulness. The other cluster is associated with
   a. the menstrual cycle
   b. the light-dark cycle
   c. the internal temperature cycle
   d. none of the above

6. In mammals, the cluster of rhythms that includes sleep/wakefulness appears to be paced by
   a. the pineal gland
   b. the suprachiasmatic nuclei
   c. the brain stem reticular formation
   d. the pituitary

7. In mammals, the cluster of rhythms that includes the REM-non-REM cycle appears to be paced by
   a. the pineal gland
   b. the suprachiasmatic nuclei
   c. the brain stem reticular formation
   d. the pituitary

8. The syndrome of delayed sleep phase insomnia can be characterized best as
   a. motivational dysfunction
   b. inappropriate phase relation between biological clock and Zeitgebers
   c. reduction of total amount of sleep time
   d. inability to synchronize to Zeitgebers

9. Sleep therapy for depression was designed to
   a. modify the lethargic behavior of the depressed patient
   b. restore rhythmicity to the abnormally nonrhythmic patient
   c. increase sleep time in an attempt to permit normal dreaming
   d. synchronize the patient's sleep-wakefulness and REM-non-REM rhythms

10. Free-running circadian rhythms
    a. are rarely exactly equal to 24 hours
    b. are the result of jet lag
    c. are the result of rotating shift work
    d. are the result of lesions that destroy the suprachiasmatic disorder

11. Which of the following should NOT be described as a phase-shift disorder
    a. jet lag
    b. rotating shift work
    c. graveyard shift work
    d. the "Monday morning blues"

12. Which of the following structures secretes hormones or neurotransmitters with a circadian rhythm
    a. adrenal medulla
    b. pineal gland
    c. raphe nuclei
    d. all of the above

13. Biological rhythms have NOT been demonstrated in
    a. plants
    b. animals
    c. rocks
    d. none of the above

14. Which of the following biological rhythms has been observed in humans?
    a. circadian rhythm of cortisol
    b. infradian rhythm of estrogen
    c. ultradian rhythm of follicle-stimulating hormone
    d. all of the above

15. At the end of his six-month stay in a cave, Siffre became confused when he was told that the experiment was finished because
    a. his "days" were longer than 24 hours
    b. of mental fatigue
    c. his rhythms had become desynchronized
    d. his "days" were shorter than 24 hours

True or False

_____ 1. Zeitgebers must by sensed by the organism.

_____ 2. Zeitgebers are necessary for the biological rhythms of one organism to be synchronized with those of another organism.

_____ 3. The dominant role of the pineal gland in behavioral rhythmicity has been observed only in birds.

_____ 4. In humans, over one hundred separate circadian rhythms have been described.

_____ 5. In humans, the highest values of all physiological systems controlled by circadian cycles, occur during the wakefull phase of the sleep-wakefulness cycle. _sleep_

_____ 6. In the presence of light-dark cycles, all circadian rhythms of normal humans are synchronized with the sleep-wakefulness cycle.

_____ 7. The suprachiasmatic nucleus of the hypothalamus paces the sleep-wakefulness cycle in all mammals that have been studied.

_____ 8. The suprachiasmatic nucleus controls the duration of the sleep period in mammals. — _senses light & dark coordinates_

_____ 9. A single 15-minute exposure to light presented in the morning causes the activity of birds to occur earlier on the following day, while the same pulse of light delays activity if it is presented in the evening.

_____ 10. The pineal gland of birds is sensitive to changes in light only during the night.

_____ 11. Zeitgebers are the sources or driving forces of biological rhythms. — _we don't know_

F _____ 12. The free-running period of circadian rhythmicity in humans has not been determined because it is impossible to remove people from all Zeitgebers. ~ (Solatio exg - caves

T _____ 13. The free-running period of circadian rhythmicity in humans is usually not equal to 24 hours.

F _____ 14. The free-running periods of all circadian rhythms are equal, which indicates that a single biological oscillator paces the rhythms.

T _____ 15. The free-running periods of temperature and sleep-wakefulness rhythms in humans can differ to the extent that "daily" maximal temperatures can occur during sleep.

Matching

d _____ 1. circadian   a. period greater than one day

g _____ 2. ultradian   b. a circadian clock w/ light, influence

a _____ 3. infradian   c. a circadian pacemaker

_____ 4. circadian phase   d. period about 24 hours long

b _____ 5. pineal gland   e. migrate twice a year

c _____ 6. suprachiasmatic nuclei   f. salient environmental cycles

f _____ 7. Zeitgeber   g. period less than one day long

_____ 8. progesterone   h. display a circadian period of 24.8 hours

h _____ 9. golden-brown algae   i. enhances estrogen action

e _____ 10. willow warblers   j. time of day

Short Answer

1. Why might a circadian system respond differentially with a phase advance to a pulse of light late at night and a phase delay to a pulse of light early at night, and what might happen if an intense light were presented in the middle of the night?

2. Give two reasons why circadian rhythmicity should be considered when administering drug treatment for infectious disease.

3. What is the selective advantage of coupling the reproductive rhythm to the circadian rhythm, and what brain structure is common to both these systems?

4. How is it possible that a person may be blind but still able to entrain to the light-dark cycle?

5. What is the primary function of a biological clock? What is the pri nary function of a central pacemaker?

ANSWERS TO SELF TEST

Multiple Choice

1. c	2. a	3. c	4. d	5. c	6. b	7. c
8. b	9. d	10. a	11. c	12. d	13. c	14. d
15. a						

True or False

1. T	2. T	3. T	4. T	5. F	6. T	7. T
8. F	9. T	10. T	11. F	12. F	13. T	14. F
15. T						

Matching

1. d
2. g
3. a
4. j
5. b
6. c
7. f
8. i
9. h
10. e

CHAPTER 7
EMOTIONS: THE HIGHS AND LOWS OF THE BRAIN

Before You Read This Chapter

OBJECTIVES

After you reading this chapter, you should be able to do the following:

1. Explain how is it possible to scientifically study emotions.

2. Describe how the scientific study of emotion has evolved gradually through the years.

3. Be able to list the specific brain areas have been implicated in the experience of emotion and emotional behavior.

4. Understand how a scientist studies something as personal and seemingly nonobjective as emotions.

5. Be able to describe the role of the autonomic nervous system in the various theories of emotional behavior.

6. Explain how the limbic system is implicated in emotional behavior.

7. Appreciate the role of the limbic system in the evolution of the human species.

8. Understand the relationship of pain to emotion.

9. Describe the neurobiological features of the pain system.

10. Be able to explain the advantages of early stress experience upon the stress response later in life.

OUTLINE

Emotion and motivation

Theories of emotion

The James-Lange theory
The Cannon-Bard theory
The Papez circuit

Brain structures that mediate emotion

> The limbic system
> Structures in the brainstem
> The cerebral cortex
> The role of the autonomic nervous system in emotion

Cognition and emotion

Aggression

> Electrode studies
> Hormones
> Neurotransmitters
> Animal studies and human aggression

Pain

> How pain is sensed
> Pain pathways to the brain
> Chemical transmission and inhibition of pain
> The role of endorphins in emotion
> Individual perception of pain

Pleasure

Stress and anxiety

> Selye's General Adaptation Syndrome
> Stress, disease, and the feeling of control
> Brain function and everyday stress

The development of emotions: An evolutionary perspective

> The limbic system and care of the young
> The limbic system and social communication

THEME

A life devoid of emotions would be a boring one. Imagine for a moment living without the exhilaration of love and infatuation, without the thrill of fast cars and daring roller coasters, without the ecstasy of winning or the agony of defeat. All of these responses represent emotional reactions to things occurring in our environment. Our daily behavior is strongly influenced by our emotional responses to events, persons, and things--the hated rival, the admired singer, the respected statesman, the feared professor.

As much as humans like to believe that they are creatures of pure reason and logic, we all know that to a very large extent we are emotional creatures whose behavior cannot be predicted by logical analysis.

What, then, is emotion and what are its brain substrates? How much do we know about emotions and their physiological underpinnings?

Most of us have experienced the physiological changes that accompany strong emotions--a pounding heart, clammy skin, butterflies in the stomach, dry mouth, shaking with anger or fear. Is this all that is meant by the physiological basis of emotions? Most of us today would intuitively respond with a resounding "no." It may then come as a surprise to learn that one of the foremost historical theories regard ing the biological basis of emotion, the James-Lange theory, proposed that the experience of emotion results from the perception of one's own physiological changes. In other words, the physical sensations such as a beating heart and dry lips are the emotional state. As the reader will learn in the text, there is a kernel of truth in the James-Lange theory. However, emotion is much more than simply detect ing and responding to one's own bodily states.

Theories of Emotion

We mentioned above that one of the first theories of emotion, the James-Lange theory, suggested that the experience of emotion results from the perception of one's own physiological changes. In the early 1900's, two scientists challenged the James-Lange theory. Cannon and Bard concluded that brain events must influence the cerebral cortex to produce the subjective experience of anger and also influence the hypothalamus, which controls the body's physiological responses. While incorrect in its details, the Cannon-Bard theory did serve to focus attention on the brain.

Within the brain the Papez circuit is generally considered to be involved with emotional behavior. The Papez circuit, most of which is contained within the limbic system, consists of a large number of interconnected structures, including the anterior thalamus, hypothal amus, amygdala, hippocampus, cingulate gyrus, fornix, septum, reticular formation, locus coeruleus, substantia nigra and the frontal lobes. Each of these interconnected brain structures has been implic ated in emotion in one way or another.

Brain Structures that Mediate Emotion

The hypothalamus directly or indirectly controls much of the activity of the body, including heart rate, respiration, and body temperature. These phenomena are known to change during states of emotional arousal. The amygdala and hippocampus are located adjacent to one another and lie just beneath the cerebral cortex. In animals, damage to the amygdala results in altered aggressive and fear behavior. In the recent past, destruction of the amygdala was performed in particu larly violent criminals. Wires were inserted into the amygdala, and an electrical current was passed to destroy this structure. This dramatic form of psychosurgery has been alleged to result in reduced aggressive and violent behavior. A highly controversial practice, psychosurgery has been criticized because unlike drug therapy, its effects cannot be reversed; once destroyed, the amygdala will not regrow.

One of the most dramatic examples of brain involvement in emotional behavior can be seen after inactivation of the frontal lobes of the cerebral cortex. A graphic demonstration of the role of the frontal cortex in emotional behavior was provided by the case history of Phineas Gage. In 1848, Mr. Gage, who was employed as a dynamite tamper, had an accident in which the dynamite tamping iron was blown through his frontal lobes. Miraculously, he managed to survive the accident, but his life was never the same. A man who was previously a respected member of society and family man, Mr. Gage became quite irascible and irresponsible after loss of the frontal lobes.

Experimental Studies of Emotion

The study of the brain substrates of emotion has employed the electrical stimulation of specific brain regions and the effects of destruction parts of the brain. Among the landmark studies utilizing electrical stimulation of the brain are those of James Olds. Olds discovered that there are certain regions in the brain, many of them in the hypothalamus and limbic system, that appear to operate as reward centers. Electrical current passed through electrodes implanted in these brain regions produced an effect that an animal worked very diligently to repeat. Humans who have experienced the equivalent of this electrical stimulation report that it is quite pleasurable and desirable. One striking and interesting possibility is that neurons in this region of the brain become activated when an individual normally encounters a pleasant state of affairs.

As is true in other areas of brain research, what we have learned from lesion experiments complements the information gained from electrical stimulation studies. The unfortunate example of Phineas Gage was mentioned earlier. More modern clinical studies of frontal lobe injury confirm that pervasive changes in mood, planning ability, and personality are typical of patients suffering damage to the frontal lobes.

The difficulty in trying to understand the role of all the various brain structures in emotional behavior is that they are all interconnected. Damage to or manipulation of one brain area will undoubtedly be reflected in altered activity in other relationships between elements. Therefore, it becomes extremely difficult to parcel out the effect of any single structure that acts as a link in the chain.

Given this situation, there are several alternative approaches that can be used to study brain involvement in emotion. These approaches generally employ chemical manipulation of the brain in an attempt to understand more about the physiological underpinnings of emotion. Neuropharmacologists and psychopharmacologists are actively studying the brain's response to tranquilizing and mood-altering drugs in an effort to understand how these drugs work and what they might reveal about the operation of brain systems in emotion.

Role of the ANS

An important component of the central nervous system in emotional behavior is the autonomic nervous system. Composed of two divisions, the sympathetic and the parasympathetic divisions, the autonomic nervous system functions mainly to regulate the internal physiological status of the body with respect to outside perturbations. You will recognize this as homeostasis. Through the action of the autonomic nervous system, we come to experience the physiological responses so familiar in emotional behavior. The autonomic nervous system provides us with a dry mouth, a beating heart, clammy skin, and other similar responses. Often controlled directly by the brain, the autonomic responses can also be triggered by hormonal influences from the adrenal gland. Since hormonal influences are dependent upon the circulatory system for delivering the hormone to its site of action, their effects are considerably slower than direct nervous system control. Most of us are familiar with the aftermath of a near-miss auto accident. The beating heart and shaking hands occur shortly after the event and continue for some time before dying away.

You may wonder about the adaptive significance of an emergency mobilizing system that comes into play long after the event has passed. One must keep in mind, however, that the nervous system has not evolved under the fast-paced influences of modern society for very long. A system that has a certain lag time before becoming maximally activated was not necessarily a hindrance in the environments in which it evolved.

Most of us strive to avoid pain whenever possible. Pain itself is not an emotion but may lead to an emotional response. Until recently the biological basis of pain was poorly understood. It was known that there exist slow and fast pathways to different portions of the brain that result in dull or sharp pains, respectively, and that the sensation of pain is quite different from the perception of pain and its emotional response. For example, patients who have undergone frontal lobe lesions can report feeling pain (sensation) quite normally, but at the same time they report that they are not particularly bothered (perception) by it.

In the last decade our understanding of the biological underpinnings of pain has undergone a revolution. It has been known for a long time that the drug morphine is a powerful agent for the alleviation of pain. It is also a powerful euphoric drug, which has led to its wide spread abuse. In the 1970's, however, it was discovered that the brain has receptors for the morphine chemical. At first this finding appeared to be a complete mystery. Why should the brain possess receptors for a chemical that is derived from a plant? It was quickly realized, however, that what was really happening was that the morphine was mimicking the action of an endogenous chemical by binding to its receptors. The unknown chemicals were given the name endorphins, for endogenous morphine-like compounds. In a relatively short time, the endorphins were isolated and studies were begun to determine where they are found in the brain and their mode of action. This exciting story is fully described in the textbook and represents a milestone in modern neurobiological research and discovery. Scientists now know that the brain manufactures its own pain killers, the endorphins, and that these agents specifically act at regions in the pain pathway. Such locations as the dorsal horn of the spinal cord and periaqueductal gray matter, a part of the brainstem, have been found to have endorphin receptors. Injections of morphine directly into these regions of the brain will reduce the subjects' responses to pain, thereby proving that these regions contain the receptors for the endogenous morphine-like compound endorphin. Interestingly, the ancient Chinese practice of acupuncture, while first believed to be fraudulent, has now been shown to work by means of triggering the endorphin system.

One might question the function of an endogenous pain killer; after all, pain is supposed to be a signal warning us of impending tissue damage. One might imagine that any diminution of that signal would remove important information about our condition. While the foregoing may have some validity, it is also true that constant and intense pain is quite incapacitating. Regulating the degree of pain we experience may allow us to escape from the pain-inducer and to begin nursing our wounds.

Stress and Anxiety

A pervasive threat posed by modern society is the state of chronic anxiety in which many people find themselves. Hans Selye has made a career of studying stress and anxiety. While the usual physiological and emotional responses to stress are adaptive and rational responses to an environmental alarm, the modern-day condition of chronic anxiety, in which the stress is never resolved or is resolved for only short periods of time, can result in unpleasant consequences, such as ulcers and mental illness. According to research done on animals, the body's stress system, or the general adaptation syndrome, to use Selye's term, is a system that benefits from previous experience. Research has shown that animals who have had successful experience with the resolution of stress when young are better equipped to respond physiologically and emotionally to a stressor when adults than are individuals raised in an isolated and protected environment. Those who have been protected when young have had no experience in coping with stress and are quite devastated when suddenly confronted by a stressor.

One of the key findings of studies of chronic anxiety is that the predictability of events in the environment is important in allowing organisms to cope with stressors. One of the most terrifying aspects of modern life is the unpredictable nature of violence, where the victim is apparently picked at random. When events are unpredictable, an individual feels that he or she has no control over the environment and that there is little that can be done for protection. As a result, he or she feels anxious.

Stanley Schachter has provided the most dramatic example of how an emotional response may be molded by culture. In his experiments, which are described in detail in the text, Schachter injected a drug that produced some of the physiological signs of an emotional response. The subjects, who were unaware of what was going on, were placed in social settings in which their interpretations of their own feelings were based upon what others said. Schachter concluded that a large part of our emotional responses to an event are based not on physiological signs but upon our cognitive evaluations of the environment at the time. To use George Mandler's example, while for some individuals the feeling of sudden loss of one's weight when riding a roller coaster can be terrifying, for others the feeling can be exhilarating.

Brain and Emotional Behavior

In this chapter we have examined the physiological basis of emotion. We have seen that there are considerable difficulties in merely defining what is meant by emotions. Historically, theories of emotion have been bases upon the autonomic nervous system manifestations of emotions, such as an accelerated heart rate and a dry mouth, and the cognitive interpretations of the emotion-producing event.

The brain regions most implicated in emotional behavior are found within the limbic lobe, a widespread series of interrelated brain structures comprising, among others, the frontal lobes, amygdala, hippocampus, hypothalamus, cingulate gyrus, and septum. Electrical stimulation of some of these structures can produce both negative and positive emotional behaviors, ranging from aggression to pleasure. The means by which these various emotional behaviors are controlled is as yet unknown.

The scientific investigation of emotional behavior is made difficult by the subjective nature of the experience itself and by the necessity of performing invasive experiments on laboratory animals that are incapable of verbalizing the experienced emotion. Scientific studies have employed the two classic means of brain investigation-- electrical stimulation and surgical removal. Currently, researchers are actively investigating the use of chemical intervention to understand more about the nature of emotion and to alleviate problems with emotional behavior in humans.

A currently accepted view of emotional behavior is that both the physiological aspects of emotion (autonomic nervous system responses) and the cognitive integration of the emotional event play a role in our response to an emotional event.

We have seen that although pain is not properly considered an emotion (it is a sensation), painful stimulation often gives rise to emotional reactions. In the past decade, considerable progress has been made in our understanding of the anatomical and chemical bases of pain perception. The existence of fast and slow pain pathways in the brain and of an endogenous pain-killing substance, endorphin, has provided the impetus for further study of pain systems and of the means for alleviation of chronic pain.

The general adaptation syndrome is the physiological response for dealing with acute stress. While the response to stress is an adaptive reaction to an environmental event that poses some difficulty for the organism, modern society often presents individuals with chronic stresses, many of which cannot be resolved and result in feel ings of anxiety. Anxiety can be quite debilitating, leading to medical and emotional problems.

Scientists are still far from a complete understanding of brain involvement in emotional behavior. The complex interactions that take place among participating brain nuclei make it difficult to trace the precise origins of emotions in the brain.

QUESTIONS TO KEEP IN MIND AS YOU READ THIS CHAPTER

1. Since emotions are such an intensely personal experience, how is it possible to study emotion from a scientific standpoint?

2. Which brain regions are the most directly linked with emotional behavior?

3. What is the adaptive significance of an endogenous system to modulate pain perception?

4. Is there is any difference in the emotional responses of animals that live in social groups as opposed to animals that are solitary?

5. Some individuals are quite "tough" with respect to their ability to withstand considerable pain. Witness, for example, the feats of Indian mystics who walk on hot coal or lie on beds of nails. What do you think might be happening in the brains of these individuals?

6. What theories do you think best explain the biological basis of emotion.

7. Stress is a problem in modern society. What can be done to help alleviate it, short of continually taking tranquilizers or other drugs?

After You Have Read the Chapter, Continue with the Following Material

STUDENT'S OUTLINE

After you have read this chapter and studied the material it contains, close the book and in the space below, using your own words, try to outline the major points of what you have just read. The basic structure of the chapter is provided below.

Emotion and motivation

Theories of emotion

Brain structures that mediate emotion

Cognition and emotion

Aggression

Pain

Pleasure

Stress and anxiety

The development of emotions: An evolutionary perspective

Now that you have attempted to outline the chapter from memory, go back to the textbook and see how accurate your recollection was. Fill in those topics that you might have missed and emphasize the points that are stressed in the textbook.

Key Terms

The following terms were introduced in this chapter. You should be sure that these terms are familiar to you and that you have their definitions well in hand.

Amygdala
Cannon-Bard theory
Cingulate gyrus
Dorsal horn
Fornix
General Adaptation Syndrome
James-Lange theory
Nociceptor
Papez circuit
Periaqueductal gray area
Psychopharmacology
Reticular formation
Valium

Multiple Choice

1. A dominant animal in a hierarchy using threats to consolidate his position, even when no other animal is being provocative, is an example of:
   a. irratative aggression
   b. territorial aggression
   c. sex-related aggression
   d. instrumental aggression

2. Neurons that specifically affect the activity of the autonomic nervous system (heart rate, respiration, etc.) appear to be concentrated in the
   a. hippocampus
   b. thalamus
   c. amygdala
   d. hypothalamus

3. The _____ plays an important role in emotion by acting as a "filter" for novel or persistent information.
   a. hippocampus
   b. hypothalamus
   c. reticular formation
   d. thalamus

4. During an emergency, the _____ nervous system is called into play.
   a. automatic
   b. autonomic
   c. independent
   d. secondary

5. The substantia nigra, or "black area," is a collection of neurons that secrete large amounts of the neurotransmitter _____.
   a. norepinephrine
   b. serotonin
   c. acetylcholine
   d. dopamine

6. Phineas Gage suffered profound emotional disruptions as a result of accidental destruction of his _____.
   a. temporal lobes
   b. occipital lobes
   c. frontal lobes
   d. parietal lobes

7. Norepinephrine (sometimes called adrenalin) is the major transmitter of the _____ nervous system.
   a. central
   b. parasympathetic
   c. empathetic
   d. sympathetic

8.   W. R. Hess found that when he stimulated a specific area of a cat's hypothalamus, it:
     a.   curled up and went to sleep
     b.   engaged in predatory aggression
     c.   stopped eating and hissed at the experimenter
     d.   showed behaviors typical of fear-provoked aggression

9.   The fundamental human emotions of happiness, disgust, and surprize are recognized across cultures by about _____ percent of those tested, suggesting that there may be an evolutionary basis to these emotions.
     a.   50-70
     b.   80-100
     c.   less than 20 %, suggesting little evolutionary basis
     d.   none of the above

10. The benzodiazepam tranquilizer Valium is thought to work by promoting the effectiveness of the neurotransmitter _____:
     a.   acetylcholine
     b.   GABA
     c.   endorphin
     d.   norepinephrine

11. The statement "we feel sorry because we cry, angry because we strike, afraid because we tremble" exemplifies the theory of emotion proposed by _____.
     a.   Cannon-Bard
     b.   James-Lange
     c.   Stanley Schachter
     d.   James Papez

12. The thesis that emotional responding requires both a physiological and a cognitive component was proposed by _____.
     a.   Papez
     b.   Freud
     c.   Schachter
     d.   Cannon

13. Which of the following is NOT a component of Selye's general stress adaptation syndrome?
     a.   alarm
     b.   resistance
     c.   extinction
     d.   exhaustion

14. Which of the following drugs is effective in reducing "anxiety" in rats?
     a.   alcohol
     b.   barbiturates
     c.   tranquilizers
     d.   all the above

15. Which of the following structures is NOT part of the limbic system:
    a. hypothalamus
    b. hippocampus
    c. amygdala
    d. locus coeruleus *brainstem*

True or False

___T___ 1. Mild emotions are rarely accompanied by recognizable physiological responses.

___T___ 2. No "one-to-one" correspondence exists between neural events in the brain and the states we experience as emotion.

___T___ 3. Scientists have not been able to agree on a clear definition of emotion.

___T___ 4. W.R. Hess showed that stimulation of centers in the hypothalamus can produce rage in an otherwise quiescent animal.

___T___ 5. Among human behaviors, smiling in greeting seems to be a genetically wired-in expression.

___T___ 6. The limbic system in the human brain does not differ vastly from that of mammals below us on the evolutionary scale.

___T___ 7. Mammals and birds are the only organisms that devote a great deal of attention to the care of their young.

___T___ 8. The fact that people from many cultures can recognize the same emotions suggests that these emotions are biologically determined.

___T___ 9. The James-Lange theory of emotion proposes that physical sensations are emotions. *no pain properties*

___F___ 10. Naloxone is a potent drug that mimics the action of morphine. *blocking agent*

___F___ 11. Pain is considered the strongest emotion. *not emotion*

___T___ 12. Pain perception differs from person to person and within any single person from time to time.

___T___ 13. Studies using radioactively labeled opiate drugs have shown that a high concentration of opiate receptors exists in the limbic system.

___F___ 14. Endorphins inhibit the release of substance P in the spinal cord. *dorsal horn*

___T___ 15. Stress is not always harmful but rather is an important part of an adaptive response to the environment.

Matching

_d_ 1. Martin Seligman   _a._ "endogenous morphine"

_i_ 2. Parkinson's disease   _b._ sympathetic-
                                               parasympathetic

_g_ 3. James Olds   _c._ Substance P

_b_ 4. autonomic nervous system   _d._ "learned helplessness"

_j_ 5. myelin   _e._ filter for novel or
                                               persistent information

_c_ 6. dorsal horn   _f._ hypothalamic rage

_h_ 7. James Papez   _g._ "pleasure centers"

_a_ 8. endorphin   _h._ "stream of feeling"

_f_ 9. W.R. Hess   _i._ L-dopa

_e_ 10. reticular formation   _j._ functions like insulator
                                               in electric wires

Short Answer

1. Briefly describe the experiments of James Olds that demonstrated the existence of "pleasure centers" in the brain.

2. List the major subdivisions of the autonomic nervous system and describe the functions of each.

3. Briefly explain the Schachter-Singer theory of emotion.

4. Describe the roles of substance P and endorphin in the modulation of pain.

5. List and define the major stages of Selye's general stress adaptation syndrome.

ANSWERS TO SELF-TEST

Multiple Choice

1. d   2. d   3. c   4. b   5. d   6. c   7. d
8. d   9. b   10. b   11. b   12. c   13. c   14. d
15. d

True or False

1. T	2. T	3. T	4. T	5. T	6. T	7. T
8. T	9. T	10. F	11. F	12. T	13. T	14. F
15. T						

Matching

1. d
2. i
3. g
4. b
5. j
6. c
7. h
8. a
9. f
10. e

CHAPTER 8
LEARNING AND MEMORY

Before You Read This Chapter

OBJECTIVES

After reading this chapter, you should be able to do the following:

1. List the different forms of learning and memory studied in the context of brain function.

2. Know the different experimental methods (ranging from the use of animal models to the study of injured humans) used to help us comprehend the workings of learning and memory in the brain.

3. Know the kinds of changes associated with learning and memory that occur in the nervous system in simple animals.

4. Identify the brain areas implicated in learning and memory.

5. List the steps in the process of forming a memory.

6. Explain the differences between immediate recall, short-term memory, and long-term memory.

7. Be able to explain brain plasticity.

8. Know the particular biochemical phenomena associated with learning and memory.

9. Distinguish between procedural and declarative memory.

10. Know the connection between reinforcing events and brain processes.

11. Distinguish the four different kinds of amnesia that have been studied in humans.

OUTLINE

Simple learning and neural changes

Habituation
Classical conditioning
  Neuroanatomical changes
  Biophysical changes in the cell membrane
  Biochemical mechanisms

Brain systems and memory

> The cerebellum
> The hippocampus
> The cortex
> Transmitter systems
> Protein synthesis

Simple learning and the human brain

The human memory system

> Information processing aspects of memory
> Short-term and long-term memory
> Memory consolidation
> Procedural and declarative memory
> Reward and punishment in learning and remembering

What can we learn from damaged brains?

> Four types of amnesia
> > Patient H.M.
> > Patient N.A.
> > Korsakoff's syndrome
> > Electroconvulsive shock therapy
> Two brain regions and their functions

The brain's plasticity: Environmental effects

THEME

What are learning and memory? Learning refers to a change in behavior and thus a change in brain function as a result of experience. Memory refers to the persistence of that change in the brain, such that future behavior may be influenced as a function of the earlier experience. Thus, learning and memory are two sides of the same coin. It is difficult to imagine memory when no learning has taken place. The opposite, learning with no memory, occurs in some of us much too frequently. Nevertheless, both phenomena are intimately related and are fundamental to the nervous system's ability to adapt to its environment.

Imagine someone totally incapable of learning or remembering. This unfortunate individual would live completely in the here and now and would have no appreciation for the everyday things that we all take for granted. Furniture, trees, dogs, cats, or friends would have no meaning because they would be unrecognized as a result of the brain's lack of memory. One would not be able to carry on conversations, to reflect, to plan or to enjoy music. All these things would be experienced anew each time they were presented. Fortunately, there are no individuals we know of who are so totally afflicted with the inability to learn and remember. There are, however, individuals who are handicapped in their learning capabilities, in their memory capabilities, or in both.

In this chapter, we examine some of the brain substrates of learning and memory. This is a relatively new field for brain science. As recently as the 1950s, brain scientists who ventured into the area of learning and memory were seen as true pioneers working in an area that would not yield to scientific advances for a long time. In the 30 years that have elapsed, we have seen that this view was wrong and that, in fact, the brain is starting to reveal its secrets of learning and memory.

Simple Learning and Neural Changes

As is true in much of neuroscience, fundamental knowledge about learning and memory has come largely through the ability to study simple organisms performing sim ple tasks. There are two reasons for this. First, a simple well-defined task has few undefined variables that can interfere with what we desire to observe. Second, a simple organism, be it a marine mollusk like *Aplysia* or a piece of brain tissue maintained in a culture tube, is nowhere near as complex as the brain of a human and thus is more amenable to analysis.

Among the simplest kinds of behavior in learning and memory is habituation. Habituation takes place when a stimulus that an organism originally responded to is presented repeatedly, and the organism stops responding to it. Humans habituate in the same way that the marine mollusk *Aplysia* habituates. The nervous system of *Aplysia*, however, is considerably simpler than that of a human, so the analysis of what is going on is much simpler for the scientist. The *Aplysia* has a reflex behavior that displays the properties of habituation. The *Aplysia* breathes through a gill, which is extended into the water to extract oxygen. If touched, the *Aplysia* withdraws the gill in a protective reflex. If touched repeatedly, however, the animal habituates and no longer withdraws its gill. Dr. Eric Kandel and his associates have studied the cellular basis for habituation in *Aplysia*. They have discovered that in the neuronal circuit that controls gill withdrawal, less neurotransmitter is released from sensory neurons to motor neurons during the process of habituation. We see that in *Aplysia*, at least, short-term habituation is the result of a decrease in excitation of synapses in an existing neural pathway between sensory and motor neurons.

A more complicated form of behavior is that popularized by Ivan Pavlov in the early 1900s. Pavlov conducted some of the first experiments in classical conditioning. Classical conditioning is a type of associative learning in which several stimuli become linked. In habituation, the organism must deal with only one stimulus. In classical conditioning, however, the organism must learn the relationship between two stimuli. Pavlov's early experiments with the salivary response in dogs showed that this simple form of learning occurs when a stimulus that initially produced salivation (food) is paired with a neutral stimulus (a bell). Eventually, the bell alone elicits the salivation. A great deal of work was done in the years following Pavlov's early demonstrations to define the conditions around which classical conditioning operates. In Pavlov's experiment, the food that elicited the salivation on its initial presentation is termed the unconditioned stimulus; the bell that initially produced no response is called the conditioned stimulus; the salivation that was elicited by the presentation of food is called the unconditioned response; and the salivation that was eventually learned in response to the bell stimulus is called the conditioned response. In the many years that have passed since Pavlov's initial observations, scientists have studied the rules that govern stimulus presentations in classical conditioning and have learned that there are many variables that are important. Among the most important is the order of presenting the stimuli to the subject. It is critical that the conditioned stimulus be presented prior to the unconditioned stimulus; that is, the bell must precede the food. In this experiment, the bell signals the presence of food; therefore, if the food were presented before the bell, the bell would not signify the presence of anything.

Although classical conditioning is well understood and actively studied in research laboratories, it is probably not terribly evident in everyday human activities. Certainly many of us have classically conditioned emotional responses to dentists, to hypodermic needles, and to angry dogs, but the bulk of our activity is governed more by rational, cognitive processes than by the simpler forms of associative learning represented by classical conditioning.

One aspect of learning that has also been identified as a critical one is the reinforcing or rewarding event. In the case of Pavlov's dog, the delivery of meat was positively reinforcing event; it was something which the dog would strive to obtain. In many other laboratory experiments, animals are confronted by an unpleasant stimulus to which they must make a certain response in order to either escape from or prevent it. In this case, the reinforcing event is the elimination of the painful stimulus or the escape from the fear that is signaled by the conditioned stimulus. In all of these cases, the stimuli produce an emotional response in the organism, and that response is associated with biochemical activation of the adrenal gland, which secretes norepinephrine. A number of individuals believe that norepinephrine plays an important role in facilitating memory consolidation. Therefore, it seems reasonable to hypothesize that norepinephrine and probably other brain chemicals are involved in the brain's mediation of reinforcing events.

Brain Systems and Memory

Neurobiologists have studied the underlying neural mechanisms of classical conditioning in another marine animal, the marine snail, *Hermissenda*. *Hermissenda* has learned to associate light with a specific movement. The work of Dan Alkon and associates has provided a description for the events that occur in the simple nervous system of this marine snail during the acquisition of this conditioned response. Changes have been found at three levels in the snail's nervous system: the anatomical, the biophysical, and the biochemical levels. These investigators discovered that neurons that are responsible for sensing the unconditioned stimulus influence neurons that are responsible for sensing the conditioned stimulus. The effect on this neuroanatomical connectivity with learning trials was to alter the excitability of the sensory cells of the conditioned stimulus. The biophysical change in the cell membrane that was eilicited by the conditioning took the form of a reduced outflow of potassium ions and an increased inflow of calcium ions. Remember that the resting potential of the neuron is critically dependent on the ratio of ions on the inside and outside of the cell and the ability of ions to flow through channels in the membrane (see Chapter 2 for review). During the acquisition of the learned response in *Hermissenda*, calcium ions accumulated within the conditioned-stimulus sensory cells. This accumulation resulted in a reduction in the number of potassium channels that were open and thus a reduced outflow of potassium from the cell. These changes, however, are only transient. The animal's behavioral change lasts considerably longer than the elevation in calcium levels seen inside the sensory cell. The long-term change in the nervous system that is responsible for the snail's memory of this learned response is a function of a particular enzyme. A phosphorylated protein channel displays different properties and may influence which ions can pass through the membrane. This change in protein phosphorylation is of relatively long duration and could account for the prolonged excitability change in the cell that underlies the behavior change. Therefore, it appears that the increased level of calcium activates the phosphorylating enzymes and that these enzymes, once activated, keep on working for a long time after calcium levels have returned to normal. We can summarize these experiments in the following way:

1. Snails were classically conditioned, and the neural changes underlying the altered behavior were studied.

2. Cells responding to the conditioned stimulus became highly excited as the result of training. The cells' excitation was associated with an outflow of potassium ions and an inflow of calcium ions.

3. This transient change was made permanent by activating a phosphorylating enzyme that changed the nature of the membrane ion channels, thus giving rise to a lasting change in the function of these cells and a relatively long-lasting change in behavior.

The neurobiology of learning and memory has not concentrated exclusively on studies of marine mollusks and snails. Studies performed primarily on rats and rabbits have implicated a couple of brain areas as critically important for certain kinds of learning and memory. The cerebellum is traditionally thought of as a motor organ that serves to coordinate the actions of muscles, resulting in smooth coordinated movement. It has recently been discovered, however, that the cerebellum is also involved in the learning of motor tasks. In an experiment by Richard Thompson and colleagues at Stanford, rabbits were classically conditioned to move their "third eyelid" in response to conditioned stimulus. The critical quesitons confronting the brain scientists are: "What is the pattern of brain activation? What is the neural circuit that is essential to the learning and performance of this task?" Using a combination of the lesion technique and of recording from various regions of the brain, researchers discovered that a particular region of the cerebellum is critically involved in the memory trace for eyelid conditioning in the rabbit. It seems probable that this portion of the cerebellum is in the critical circuit for the learning of this response.

Human Learning

While the involvement of the cerebellum in learning and memory came as a surprise to many scientists working in this area, the role of the hippocampus in learning and memory has been suspected for many years. Humans suffering damage to this structure have been observed to have considerable difficulty recalling things they learned after the injury occurred. The best-studied human patient with hippocampal damage is H.M., whom we will discuss in more detail later on. Animal studies on learning and memory support the view obtained from humans that the hippocampus is critically involved. In the eyelid learning experiment in the rabbit referred to earlier, electrodes recording the activity of neurons in the rabbit hippocampus denoted activity when the conditioned stimulus was applied. A promising neurophysiological mechanism for memory in the hippocampus is seen in the form of a phenomenon known as long-term potentiation. Long-term potentiation is seen in hippocampal synapses when an animal success fully learns in a behavioral learning experiment. The change in synaptic efficacy between two neurons in the hippocampus has been observed to last for very long periods of time, up to months in certain experiments. Although it has not been proved, many believe that long-term potentiation is a promising model for information stor age in the vertebrate brain. The actual mechanisms underlying long-term potentiation are structural changes in the synaptic regions of hippocampal neurons that are associated with increased effectiveness of these synapses.

The Human Memory System

Human behavior, of course, is regulated more by higher cortical func tions than it is by habituation and classical conditioning. There is very little question that the cortex must be critically involved in information storage and analysis. However, at this time we do not have the ability to say exactly what those changes might be. It is known that the brain is quite flexible and that the cortex, in partic- ular, shows a high degree of responsiveness to changes in environment. In experiments done at the University of California, Berkeley, rats were raised in both enriched and impoverished environments, and it was demonstrated quite clearly that the brain responds to these alterations in its environment by changes in its structure, its chemistry, and presumably its function as well.

Of course, it is unethical to experimentally expose humans to an impoverished environment. However, occasionally such situations do occur, as is documented in the text in the case of Genie. From the story of Genie it can be inferred that prolonged isolation from a normal environment can produce irreversible changes in the brain. This unfortunate youngster was isolated from a normal environment until she was 13 years old, unable "catch up" to a normal teenager, displaying language and cognitive abilities consistent with those of a very young child. This suggests that the brain does not remain plastic forever, and that if the right kind of environmental influences are not present during brain development, the structure and function of the brain will be permanently impaired.

What can one say regarding human learning and memory from the studies that neurobiologists have conducted on marine snails and mollusks? The basic assumption is that nervous systems of all creatures operate according to more or less the same rules. Therefore, neural processes that mediate memory at the level of a simpler organism may well occur in a more complex organism. The burden of proof, of course, is on the scientist, who cannot take these assumptions for granted but must prove them.

The Organization of Memory

How is memory organized in the brain? It's one thing to understand something about what changes in particular synapses when memory is encoded, and quite another thing to understand how memories are organized in the brain, how they are stored, and how they are retrieved. One of the early attempts at trying to unravel this mystery was by Karl Lashley, a pioneer in these studies at Harvard Univerity. Lashley attempted to disrupt whatever organization he thought existed in the brain by creating lesions in the cortex of a rat. Much to his surprise, Lashley discovered that he was unable to find a specific location where the memory trace, which is termed the engram, was located. This gave rise to the idea that there is no one single location that stores memories but that information is stored in many areas of the brain simultaneously. One of the more influential theories of brain function was that of Donald Hebb of Canada. Hebb clearly explained the difference between short-term memory and long-term memory. He believed that short-term memory was encoded by patterns of activity looping through the brain in structures he termed the cell assembly. Long-term memory, according to Hebb, involved structural changes of synaptic regions, such as has been observed to occur as a consequence of long-term potentiation.

The division between short-term and long-term memory is an important one to grasp. There actually are several kinds of short-term memory. The shortest of them is called immediate memory and lasts for only a few seconds. The longer variety lasts up to minutes and is the kind of memory utilized when looking up a telephone number in a phone book, dialing it and then forgetting the number shortly afterward. The nature of short-term memory has been well studied by psychologists in terms of temporal characteristics of the storage as well as of the capacity of the stored short-term memory. It is no accident that the telephone company employs seven-digit numbers, because it was discovered that seven items (+/- two) is the practical limit for short-term memory storage capacity. Long-term memory is, of course, quite long and can extend for many decades in the human. The patient H.M., referred to earlier, who underwent surgical removal of his hippocampus, is unable to store items in long-term memory. H.M. apparently has a quite intact short-term memory, but he is unable to convert short-term storage into long-term memories. The consequence of this is that H.M. lives entirely in the present. One fascinating aspect of H.M.'s problem is that his memory deficit is not universal; that is, he can learn and retain motor tasks, such as riding a bicycle, at a level comparable to that of a normal individual. It's only when H.M. is asked to recall or recognize experiences from the recent past that the deficit shows up.

These distinctions between the kinds of memory operations observed in animals and humans have led to the conceptual distinction between procedural and declarative memory. Procedural memory refers to "how to" processes, whereas declarative memory refers to "what" memories. Stated another way, procedural memory is related to learning and remembering how to do things, whereas decalarative memory refers to remembering facts about the world. It has been suggested that one of the main reaons why most of us are unable to remember events from our early childhood is that during this period of our lives the brain is devoted almost exclusively to procedural knowledge or to learning how to coordinate muscles, how to judge the relative size of objects, and how to connect cause and effect. Only later in life do the brain circuits and processes underlying declarative knowledge come on-line, allowing individuals to have memory of early events. These ideas fit quite nicely with the developmental ideas of Jean Piaget.

Earlier we spoke of the role of reward and punishment in learning and remembering and assigned to it a critical position in the phenomenon of memory. The work of James McGaugh suggests a possible physiological basis for reinforcements in operant conditioning. McGaugh and his coworkers have discovered that certain operations and treatments can produce amnesia following learning. One of the most exciting observations was of treatments that interfered with the activity of the brain area known as the amygdala and with circulating epinephrine and norepinephrine from the adrenal glands. The results of these experiments suggest that the process of consolidation from short-term to long-term memory may involve the influence of the amygdala, which in turn is triggered by circulating hormones, primarily norepinephrine, that are secreted by the adrenal glands.

What Can We Learn from Damaged Brains

While we do not yet understand the organization or the details of the mechanism of operation of human memory, we do know something about memory and its brain substrates from the study of damaged human brains. Amnesia can take many forms, but it rarely afflicts all memories--rather, it is selective. We saw earlier that the patient H.M. cannot remember new information that has occurred since his surgery although his memory for events that preceded his surgery is normal. H.M. cannot remember facts about the world, but he can learn how to do new things; in other words, H.M. has a defect in declarative memory, but his procedural memory appears intact.

Another patient known as N.A. suffered brain damage to one of the nuclei of his thalamus. His amnesia seems to be specifically related to verbal and written material. He is able to remember faces and spatial locations but fails to remember lists of words and prose. One of the more common forms of amnesia is Korsakoff's syndrome, which is associated with chronic alcoholism. Those who are suffering from Korsakoff's disease (which also reflects a vitamin B_1 deficiency) not only have difficulty remembering current events but are impaired in their ability to recall events from early in their lives. The brain damage seen in Korsakoff patients is relatively widespread, including the thalamic nuclei, the cortex and the cerebellum.

Still another kind of amnesia commonly seen in humans is associated with electroconvulsive shock therapy, which is given to patients suffering from severe cases of depression. Following the shock therapy, patients usually report amnesia for the events preceding the shock, but this gradually disappears, allowing those memories to reappear.

These various kinds of amnesia suggest that two different regions of the brain may be involved in declarative and procedural memory. The hippocampus, amygdala, and related structures may well be involved in memory consolidation and the transfer of declarative memory to long-term storage. Another region of the brain, containing the thalamus and the frontal lobes of the cortex, may be necessary for the initial coding of certain kinds of declarative in formation. While these are interesting hypotheses and are supported to some extent by scientific findings, we are only at the beginning of studies into the neural basis of learning and memory and that we can expect to see rapid progress in this field in the coming decades.

As you read in more detail about the ideas and experiments reviewed above, keep in mind the overall theme of this book--that all that we do in health or sickness is the result of the interactions of countless millions or billions of neurons operating according to relatively simple rules. The brain is beginning to divulge its secrets about learning and memory to the scientist.

Brain Structures of Learning and Memory

In this chapter we have investigated the brain substrates of learning and memory. The main point to extract from a study of the material in this section is an appreciation of the simple forms of learning and their corresponding neural changes, which have been well studied in the laboratory. Such studies have led to significant insights into the brain processes of habituation, classical conditioning, and operant condtioning. Most of the scientific advances in our understanding of the brain's plasticity have come from scientists working on simpler organisms performing simpler tasks. We know a good deal of the under lying neurobiology of habituation from studying the behavioral and neural responses of the marine mollusk *Aplysia* in a behavioral habituation task. We know that in this simple form of learning, what is happening at the neuronal level is a decrease in the amount of neurotransmitter released into the synapse after repeated stimulation.

The marine snail *Hermissenda* has been extensively studied in order to learn about the neural mechanisms underlying classical conditioning. These studies tell us that those neurons that respond to the unconditioned stimulus influence the neurons that respond to the conditioned stimulus in such a way that the excitability of the latter neurons is increased. We know that this increased excitability is caused by the movement of ions across the membrane, a transient event made permanent by the activation of a phosphorylating enzyme that permanently alters the characteristics of the ion channels in the membrane.

Somewhat removed from simple systems and the simplest forms of learning in *Aplysia* and *Hermissenda* are the brain systems involved in learning and memory in mammals: the cerebellum and the hippocampus. Case studies of human beings have shown that individuals deprived of their hippocampi (like H. M.) lose the ability to encode information into long-term memory, and thus they continually live in the here and now. Similarly, animal studies involving recording from cells in the hippocampus show that this structure is active during some forms of classical conditioning. The exact role that the hippocampus plays in memory is not known, but it seems certain that other regions of the brain are involved as well.

Probably the most surprising recent finding about the neural correlates of learning and memory has been the critical role played by the cerebellum in certain forms of classical conditioning. Long regarded as a motor modulatory and movement coordination center, the cerebellum has recently been shown to be critically involved in a neurocircuit that enables classically conditioned eyelid responses in rabbits. Discrete lesions to specific locations in the cerebellum result in an inability to perform in this situation, but the ability to perform in other learning environments remains intact.

The role of brain biochemistry and neurochemistry in learning and memory has been studied for a long time. Clearly, there is biochemical and neurochemical involvement when learning occurs. The difficult part is to distinguish which changes occur exclusively during learning and memory and which changes are normal constituents of brain activity. Several neurotransmitters have been identified as playing critical roles in learning and memory. Norepinephrine has been shown to be an effective modulator of memory mechanisms, either when administered directly or when manipulated in conjunction with other drugs. The neurotransmitter acetylcholine has been implicated in learning and memory but plays a somewhat different role. Many researchers think that loss of acetylcholine activity underlies many of the serious forms of dementia seen in older people.

Protein synthesis, and all that it implies, including the build ing of new structures, is widely thought to be involved in the processes of learning and memory. When given in large enough doses, protein synthesis inhibitors will interfere with learning and memory. While there is sound evidence that protein synthesis is involved in aspects of learning and memory, the difficulty is in distinguishing protein synthesis changes induced by learning and memory from those induced by brain activity in general.

It is well established that many components of the brain are responsive to environmental change. The experiments utilizing enriched and impoverished environments have shown quite clearly that when placed in an enriched and challenging envronment, the brain responds by growing more processes and synthesizing more neurotransmitters. Conversely, when placed in an impoverished environment, the brain processes that would normally develop are severely impaired to the point where they may never recover, even given the exposure to an appropriate environ ment later on. In many ways, this interaction between environment and brain is a prototype for all forms of learning and plastic change. A critical question is: "What is the optimal environment for the developing brain?" At this point in the development of the neurosciences, that question cannot be answered fully.

When considering the organization of human memory, there are several striking questions that have yet to be answered. One regards the location of the plastic change in the brain for any given memory. This hypothetical brain change is termed the engram. The current view is that there are many locations in the brain that are altered as a result of learning.

While no one has yet claimed to have run out of long-term memory storage capacity (although one may get rather inefficient at using what is there), there is a definite size capacity in short-term memory. The main reason the telephone company employs seven-digit telephone numbers is that behavioral scientists learned long ago that this was the practical limit for the capacity of the short-term memory system that operates when one looks up a phone number and then goes to the phone to dial it. Numbers longer than seven digits would not be retained with sufficient accuracy to allow people to use them in a practical application.

Not too many years ago most brain scientists would not have thought it possible that the brain would reveal the mechanisms underlying learning and memory. Yet that is just what is beginning to happen.

QUESTIONS TO KEEP IN MIND AS YOU READ THIS CHAPTER

1. A favorite theme of television dramas is a person with amnesia and the traumas that he or she goes through in regaining the use of memory. As you read this chapter, reflect on the issues that are involved and keep in mind that the dramatizations of amnesia that you have seen may not have been accurate.

2. In this chapter you will learn about memory consolidation--a process in which information goes from short-term temporary storage in the brain to long-term permanent storage. Try to imagine what life would be like without the ability to use either short-term or long-term memory. In the chapter, you will encounter several examples of individuals who have lost parts of their memory.

3. In considering the topics of memory and learning, we again are faced with the ethical and practical dilemma inherent in neuroscience. The neuroscientist cannot directly study the human brain but must study the brains of simpler organisms that perform simpler tasks. Consider some of the limitations of this state of affairs.

4. By now you should have a good appreciation for the basic brain processes and functions. If you wished to devise a means of permanently storing information in the brain, how would you go about it? Compare your ideas with the processes that the neuroscientist has discovered to be in effect.

5. In an effort to simplify and achieve understanding, the scientist often employs very simple forms of learning in the laboratory. Such phenomena as habituation and classical conditioning have been studied by behavioral scientists and neuroscientists world-wide. Since it is probably true that these forms of behavior play a minor role in the lives of most of us, can you justify all the time and effort spent in studying them?

6. Some pharmacologists have been actively investigating chemicals that enhance or interfere with learning and memory. If such a drug were to be developed and had no serious side-effects, what changes might this bring about in our individual lives and in society in general?

7. We are continually bombarded with sensory information, yet how much of this daily detail will we remember in a week, a year, or a decade? Clearly, we will remember some of it. Can you identify which aspects will be retained in memory and which will fail to be encoded? What kind of a brain system might be operative to enable this process to work?

8. Consider these statements.
    The fact that we do not find humans or animals who are totally incapable of learning anything or of remembering any detail for a length of time suggests one of two things: either the inability to learn and to remember is incompatible with life and therefore such individuals simply do not survive, or the underlying biological mechanisms are intimately tied up with the normal processes of brain activity and are present whenever a brain is active. Do you agree with them?

After You Have Read the Chapter, Continue with the Following Material

STUDENT'S OUTLINE

After you have read the chapter and studied the material that it contains, close the book and in the space below using your own words, try to outline the major points of what you have just read. The basic structure of the chapter is provided below.

Simple learning and neural changes

Brain systems and memory

Simple learning and the human brain

The human memory system

What can we learn from damaged brains?

The brain's plasticity: Environmental effects

Now that you have attempted to outline the chapter from memory, go back to the textbook and see how accurate your recollection was. Fill in those topics that you might have missed and emphasize the points that are stressed in the textbook.

Key Terms

The following terms are introduced in this chapter. You should be sure that these terms are familiar to you and that you have their definitions well in hand.

Amphetamine
Classical conditioning
Conditioned response
Conditioned stimulus
Habituation
Immediate memory
Imprinting
Korsakoff's syndrome
Long-term memory
Memory consolidation
Mnemonic devices
Oddity problem
Operant conditioning
Phosphorylation
Proactive inhibition
Procedural knowledge
Sensitization
Short-term memory
Unconditioned response
Unconditioned stimulus

SELF-TEST

Multiple Choice

1. The simplest form of learning is
   a. classical conditioning
   b. cohabitation
   c. habituation
   d. operant conditioning

116

2. Habituation of the gill withdrawal reflex in *Aplysia* is due to
   a. increased release of inhibitory transmitter
   b. increased release of excitatory transmitter
   c. release of habituation
   d. none of the above

3. The first experiments on classical conditioning were conducted by
   a. Chekov
   b. Pavlov
   c. Skinner
   d. Watson

4. In Pavlov's classic studies, the bell is the
   a. conditioned response
   b. conditioned stimulus
   c. unconditioned response
   d. unconditioned stimulus

5. At birth the human infant's brain is about _____ of its adult size.
   a. 10%
   b. 25%
   c. 50%
   d. 75%

6. Skinner termed behaviors that an organism performs voluntarily and naturally
   a. classical behaviors
   b. conditioned behaviors
   c. operant behaviors
   d. organic behaviors

7. The patients H.M. and N.A. are similar in that they forget
   a. abnormally rapidly
   b. abnormally slowly
   c. at a normal rate
   d. none of the above

8. The pairing of light and turbulence in *Hermissenda* leads to decreased rate of movement:
   a. towards light
   b. towards turbulence
   c. towards turbulence during the presence of light
   d. all of the above

9. After conditioning in *Hermissenda*, certain photoreceptor cells display decreased potassium outflow during depolarization. This causes the cells to be
   a. less excitable
   b. more excitable
   c. totally unresponsive
   d. downright indignant

10. After classical conditioning of the rabbit eyelid response (right eye), a lesion in the right cerebellum abolishes the
    a. conditioned stimulus
    b. conditioned response (left eye)
    c. conditioned response (right eye)
    d. unconditioned response (right eye)

11. Chicks will demonstrate imprinting to
    a. mechanical toys
    b. their mother
    c. animal behavior researchers
    d. all of the above

12. The term "seven plus or minus two" refers to the number of
    a. players on a softball team
    b. seperate items that can be maintained in short-term memory
    c. seperate items that can be maintained in immediate memory
    d. neurons in a cell assembly

13. N.A.'s amnesia is thought to be due to an injury in
    a. the amygdala
    b. the hippocampus
    c. thalamic nucleus
    d. zona incerta

14. Patients with Korsakoff's syndrome and those with frontal lobe damage often demonstrate a deficit not shared by H.M. or N.A.
    a. inability to learn new material
    b. inability to control the activity in the non-dominant hemisphere
    c. perseverance in problem solving
    d. none of the above

15. Habituation and classical conditioning are examples of
    a. conceptual learning
    b. declarative learning
    c. procedural learning
    d. none of the above

True or False

_____ 1. Experience can modify the nervous system.

_____ 2. A human does not demonstrate learning during the first postnatal year.

_____ 3. Human newborns demonstrate habituation.

_____ 4. Cerebellar lesions that eliminate the conditioned eye-blink response also abolish the unconditioned response.

_____ 5. The hippocampus, which is involved in learning and memory, is necessary for classical conditioning of the eyelid response.

_____ 6. Mice raised in a "natural" setting show greater brain development than their littermates raised in an "impoverished" environment.

_____ 7. The human patient H.M. suffers from the inability to recall any events that occurred prior to his surgery. *hippoca...* *short→lo...*

_____ 8. H.M. and patients with Korsakoff's syndrome forget at a normal rate. *fast*

_____ 9. Patients H.M. and N.A. are interesting because they demonstrate different amnesic deficits from identical lesions.

_____ 10. The photoreceptors in *Hermissenda* have strictly excitatory effects.

_____ 11. Hebb's notion of the "cell assembly" proposes that memory is a process involving the interaction of many neurons.

_____ 12. In classical conditioning, the previously neutral stimulus is called the unconditioned stimulus.

_____ 13. After conditioning in *Hermissenda* , the calcium concentration in the photoreceptor cells quickly returns to normal, even though the learned behavior lasts for weeks.

_____ 14. Cerebellar lesions prevent relearning of the classically conditioned eyelid response on the same side as the lesion.

_____ 15. H.M.'s deficits reflect an inability to process "procedural" information.

Matching

_____ 1. Skinner

_____ 2. Hebb

_____ 3. engram

_____ 4. Pavlov

_____ 5. Korsakoff's syndrome

_____ 6. patient N.A.

_____ 7. patient H.M.

_____ 8. habituation

a. isolation

b. classical conditioning

c. operant conditioning

d. memory trace

e. associative learning

f. vitamin B deficiency

g. cell assembly

h. non-associative learning

9.   classical conditioning   i. rapid rate of forgetting

10.   Genie   j. thalamic lesion

Short Answer

1.   Why study simple learning in organisms with relatively simple
        nervous systems?

2.   What is unusual about H.M.'s ability to learn?

3.   What is the principle of operant conditioning?

4.   What evidence suggests that memory consolidation may take a
        number of years.

5.   How might membrane proteins be involved in the processes of
        learning and memory?

ANSWERS TO SELF-TEST

Multiple Choice

1. c	2. d	3. b	4. b	5. b	6. c	7. a
8. a	9. b	10. c	11. d	12. b	13. c	14. c
15. c						

True or False

1. T	2. F	3. T	4. F	5. F	6. T	7. F
8. F	9. F	10. F	11. T	12. F	13. T	14. T
15. F						

Matching

1.   c
2.   g
3.   d.
4.   b
5.   f
6.   j
7.   i
8.   h
9.   e
10.   a

CHAPTER 9
THINKING AND CONSCIOUSNESS

Before You Read This Chapter

OBJECTIVES

After you reading this chapter, you should be able to do the following:

1. Define the term "consciousness."

2. Explain why animals and infants do not possess consciousness as it is known in the adult human form.

3. Appreciate that conscious awareness is the processing of thought through language.

4. Understand the arguement that consciousness is not unitary. Describe this evidence and how it relates to normal individuals.

5. Describe the different functions ascribed to the left and right hemispheres of the brain.

6. Appreciate the language asymmetry of the normal brain.

7. Be familiar with Broca's aphasia and Wernicke's aphasia.

8. Know what is meant by the term "dyslexia" and the different forms it takes, and the probable underlying causes of the dysfunction.

9. Know the meaning and implications of the neglect syndrome.

10. Damage to the brain can produce quite severe symptoms that remain permanent in some and can be relatively quickly reversed in others. Understand the different conditions that lead to these outcomes.

OUTLINE

Anatomy and mind

    Association cortex
    Columns of neurons and consciousness
    The cerebral hemispheres

The bisected brain

Hemispheric specialization and consciousness

 The left hemisphere and language
  Brain sites that function in language
  Dyslexia
  Sign language
 The right hemisphere
  Visual and spatial processes
  Musical processes
 Two hemispheres: One brain

The anatomy and physiology of hemispheric differences

Patient P.S.: Language and cognitive dissonance

Conscious and nonconscious information processing

 The neglect syndrome
 Consciousness and emotion

Cortex, consciousness, and self

THEME

In this chapter, we investigate thinking and consciousness, both from a phenomenological point of view and with respect to the underlying brain processes involved. You should be aware that this is an area in which the neuroscientists are relatively ignorant. Part of this ignorance derives from the fact that animals do not display consciousness, thus the animal experiments that have led to insights into other brain processes are not possible. We shall examine the reason for this viewpoint. First, however we should define consciousness and thinking.

 While consciousness is a difficult term to define precisely, a useful definition is "awareness of one's own mental and/or physical actions...processed through the brain's language system." All of us have some intuitive feeling as to what is meant by consciousness and alterations in consciousness. We alter our state of consciousness daily when we go to sleep, when we awaken, or when we ingest too much alcohol. Therefore, consciousness can be modified by either naturally occurring or exogenous agents. As is consistent with the theme of this entire course, we assert that consciousness and thinking, like all other functions of the brain, are ultimately explainable in terms of the actions of nerve cells and the activities of nerve circuits.

Anatomy and Mind

One of the first questions about consciousness is to determine which organisms possess it. This, however, is not an easy task, because consciousness does not produce any overt behavioral signs indicating its presence. The text presents the thesis that the association cortex is responsible for the brain processes underlying consciousness. Since most non-human animals posses relatively little association cortex, they do not posses consciousness. Species that do possess sizable amounts of association cortex, notably primates such as the rhesus monkey, the chimpanzee, and the gorilla may approach some form of consciousness akin to that experienced by humans.

If animals do not posses consciousness, do human infants? It has been argued that the newborn child does not possess consciousness and, in fact, has a difficult enough time just organizing reflexes and motor activities. The full development of consciousness does not appear until the child has developed language and experience with the world. Again we return to the central definition of consciousness--an ability to think about one's own self--an ability that requires language for its operation.

The work and theories of Vernon Mountcastle suggest the way the association cortex may process consciousness. The cortex is composed of vertically interrelated neurons--called minicolumns--which, when interconnected, form columns that represent the fundamental information-processing units of the cortex. Recording of neural activity in the parietal cortex of behaving monkeys showed that different sets of columns were active during the performance of different behaviors. Mountcastle theorizes that information flow through the columns of the cortex may follow a number of different paths. It is the dominance of one path or another in this distributed system that determines what sort of processing occurs. This distributed information-processing system has inputs from the outside world, from internally generated information (termed reentrant information), and has access to numerous output systems. Whether the human brain operates similarly is unknown and will be difficult to establish given the impossibility of human experimentation.

The Bisected Brain

One of the most remarkable findings in neurobiology over the past decade is that consciousness is not a unitary phenomenon. Dr. Roger Sperry studied patients suffering from severe epilepsy who had their cerebral hemispheres surgically separated (by cutting the corpus callosum). These patients displayed different forms of consciousness in each of their disconnected hemispheres. (At this point you might wish to return to Chapters 1 and 2 to review the anatomy of the brain, the role of the corpus callosum in linking the two hemispheres, and the nature of sensory and motor crossing in the nervous system.) Only a small number of patients underwent the "split brain" operation, but the results have been quite illuminating. On first examination it is difficult, if not impossible, to differentiate a split-brain patient from a normal individual. The intelligence, personality, emotional behavior, and motor acts of these patients are normal. The differences between split-brain patients and those with intact brains becomes apparent only when specialized testing, which routes information into one or the other of the hemispheres of the brain, is employed. What has been learned from these patients and confirmed in normal individuals is that the two hemispheres are not functionally identical; rather, they display some unique capabilities. In general, the left hemisphere is primarily involved with language, speech, and other analytic, rule-governed processes. The right hemisphere, on the other hand, appears to be involved in visual and spatial processing. While the left hemisphere appears to process information in sequential manner, as would be the case with language, the right hemisphere appears to process information simultaneously, as would be the case in spatial information processing.

Hemispheric Specialization

One test has been developed for the determination of the functions of the two hemispheres is called the Wada test. It involves the injection of an anesthetic into the artery supplying either the right or left side of the brain--thus anesthetizing that hemisphere and allowing neuroscientists to observe which functions are lost. The Wada test and other forms of clinical evaluation have demonstrated that language function is unequally distributed across the two hemispheres of the brain in most individuals. The vast majority of the population is right-handed, and for most of them (95%) the language cortex can be found in the left hemisphere (the hemisphere controlling language is often termed the "dominant hemisphere"). With some right-handed individuals, however, as well as for left-handed or mixed dominant individuals, the site of the language cortex is more difficult to predict.

Because damage to regions of the cortex responsible for language produces an easily observable defect in spoken or other communicative language, we know a good deal about the neurological substrates of language. There appear to be two primary regions in the left hemisphere that are responsible for the receipt, processing, and production of language. Wernicke's area (the posterior language cortex) is primarily concerned with the receipt and understanding of language. Broca's area (the anterior language cortex) is more involved with the production of language. Injury to or disease in either of these areas of the brain results in different forms of language difficulties-- conditions known as "aphasia."

Wernicke's aphasia is characterized by a difficulty in comprehending speech and in producing meaningful language. The textbook provides an example of the kind of language produced by an individual suffering from Wernicke's aphasia. If one does not listen carefully to these individuals, the flow and fluency of language appear to be normal. Only after listening to the content do you realize what you are hearing is a "word salad" without meaning. In Broca's aphasia, on the other hand, the meaning of the individual's communication is retained, but there is an impairment in producing the sounds of speech. The spoken language of an individual suffering from Broca's aphasia is slow and labored, and although content is normal, the speech is clearly deficient in fluidity. There are a number of other forms of aphasia that are related to damage to specific regions of the brain and to a specific fiber pathway connecting Broca's and Wernicke's areas (the arcuate fasciculus). These are described in Table 9.1 in the text.

A great deal can be learned about the brain's organization of language and of other complex cognitive phenomena from studying Japanese and Chinese languages. As is discussed in the text, the Japanese language possesses two different forms of symbols, one of which is pictorial (kanji), while the other is more similar to our alphabet (kana). From studies of Japanese victims of brain damage, as well as from electrical recordings from the scalps of individuals skilled in these Japanese languages, it has been shown that damage to the left hemisphere results in an inability to read kana but a retention of the ability to read kanji. This observation is consistent with our earlier description of the functional differences between the two hemispheres in that kana is a more sequential form of communication, whereas kanji utilizes the spatial ideograph to represent a thing or concept.

Deaf individuals who use sign language often suffer the same kinds of aphasic impairments following cortical brain damage as do individuals who are able to use spoken language. It appears that the brain circuits responsible for language are largely the same regardless of the ultimate expression of that language.

When reading this chapter, you should keep in mind that most people have an intact corpus callosum and no cortical damage. Normally, the right and left hemispheres work together to analyze all the aspects of an event. It is clearly incorrect to think that when we are using language one or the other hemisphere is inactive.

Hemispheric Dysfunction

Dyslexia refers to a specific impairment in reading ability. Not related to intelligence or disturbances of spoken language, individuals are dyslexic to varying degrees, as the condition manifests itself in different ways in different people. The underlying causes of dyslexia are probably also diverse; for some individuals dyslexia may involve a visual and spatial dysfunction, whereas for others it may relate to unstable eye dominance. It has been discovered that there were microscopic alterations in cortical structure of one dyslexic, suggesting that developmental abnormalities might underlie the disturbance.

Patients with extensive damage to the right parieto-occipital cortex behave as if the left side of their bodies, and the left side of space, do not exist--the "neglect syndrome." That the syndrome is one of a disturbance of consciousness, as opposed to a sensory disorder, was demonstrated in a number of ways, as is discussed in the text. Even though these patients consciously neglect the left half of themselves and the world they can be shown to have received and processed this information--although it is inaccessible to consciousness. Joseph LeDoux believes that many emotional reactions also take place without being consciously encoded.

The Anatomy of Hemispheric Differences

Since it has been well documented that there are functional differences between the hemispheres, it has been asked whether there are also anatomical differences between them. Some regions of the brain do not demonstrate any significant differences in size between right and left halves, but other regions, such as the planum temporale (a region of the temporal lobe including Wernicke's area), do show a right-left difference in many individuals, with the left hemisphere being significantly larger. Anatomical differences such as these have been seen even in fetal humans, suggesting that the differences are genetically determined and are not the result of experience. Perhaps even more fascinating is the observation from the fossil record that the skulls of our ancestors also show anatomical asymmetries between the hemispheres.   In this chapter, we explore several areas of mental activity for which the neurosciences can only begin to provide an explanation. These areas of almost exclusively human endeavor represent the highest plane of brain function and yet are some of the most mysterious in terms of their underlying mechanism of operation. No neuroscientist today can begin to describe in detail the brain mechanisms that occur when an individual utilizes language.   This is fertile ground for future research in the neurosciences, as scientists begin to investigate in detail the brain mechanisms that underlie these complex functions.

QUESTIONS TO KEEP IN MIND AS YOU READ THIS CHAPTER

1.   How can the study of consciousness and thinking, which are be hidden from view, be approached scientifically?

2.   The position taken in this chapter is that animals do not display consciousness.   Some may argue with this position. How might you resolve the issue?

3.   Do you agree that consciousness and intelligence represent two quite different capabilities?

4.   Can you determine which hemisphere of the brain is more engaged at any given point in time during the day? Is this a valid question to ask?

5.   Can you describe anatomy of inputs and outputs to the brain that are separated in the "split-brain" patients?

6.   Given what you have learned about the operation of the intact brain, how would you respond to a suggestion to revise the educational process to better accommodate students judged to be predominantly right- or left-brained?

7.   A child suffering from brain damage may recover language ability much more readily than an adult. Why?

8.   Can you identify examples of nonconscious information processing in your own behavior?

STUDENT'S OUTLINE

Anatomy and mind

The bisected brain

Hemispheric specialization and consciousness

The anatomy and physiology of hemispheric differences

Patient P.S.: Language and cognitive dissonance

Conscious and nonconscious information processing

Cortex, consciousness, and self

Now that you have attempted to outline this chapter from memory, go back to the textbook and see how accurate your recollection was. Fill in those topics you might have missed and emphasize the points that are stressed in the textbook.

Key Terms

The following terms were introduced in this chapter. You should be sure that these terms are familiar to you and that you have their definitions well in hand.

Aphasia
Arcuate fasciculus
Association cortex
Broca's area

Cognitive dissonance
Consciousness
Corpus callosum
Cross cuing
Declarative knowledge
Dyslexia
Evoked potential
Minicolumn
Neglect syndrome
Neocortex
Planum temporale
Sylvian fissure
Tachistoscope
Wada test
Wernicke's area
Z lens

SELF-TEST

Multiple Choice

1. The most dramatic difference between the brains of reptiles and amphibians and the brains of mammals is the development of the
   a. neocortex
   b. cerebellum
   c. temporal lobe
   d. brain stem

2. With respect to consciousness, which of the following is correct?
   a. common among primates
   b. depends upon the development of language
   c. all actions require consciousness
   d. appears at sexual maturity

3. The right hemisphere controls sensing and movement on the _____ of the body.
   a. left side
   b. right side
   c. front
   d. back

4. The neocortex in rats and cats is largely occupied by areas given over to
   a. thinking and consciousness
   b. hunger and thirst
   c. sensing and movement
   d. sleeping and mating

5. The cortical lobes of the human brain that contain association cortex are
   a. frontal, parietal
   b. temporal, occipital
   c. frontal, parietal, temporal
   d. frontal, parietal, temporal, occipital

6. A specific impairment in producing speech, though language comprehension remains normal, describes a disorder known as
   a. Broca's aphasia
   b. Wernicke's aphasia
   c. jargon aphasia
   d. conduction aphasia

7. Association areas in the parietal cortex
   a. are found only in monkeys
   b. synthesize somatosensory, visual and auditory information
   c. mediate decisions about what actions to take
   d. along with those in frontal and occipital lobes, are
      involved with language processing

8. The basic unit of the cortex is the minicolumn, it is
   a. virtually identical in size in all parts of cortex
   b. present only in association cortex
   c. composed of about 10,000 neurons
   d. specialized into sensory, processing, or output functions

9. Which of the following is NOT true of dyslexia:
   a. tends to run in families
   b. tends to be associated with left handedness
   c. is more common in boys
   d. can often lead to aphasia

10. With respect to the operation of Mountcastle's distributed system of cortical information processing, internally generated information--memories, emotions, cognitive skills-- is known as
    a. local-circuit information
    b. homeostatic information
    c. reentrant information
    d. associative information

11. _____ can be conceived of as an electrical or neural storm in the brain.
    a. Alzheimer's disease
    b. Consciousness
    c. Fainting
    d. Epilepsy

12. The unique aspect of the split-brain patient P.S., who could communicate with either isolated hemisphere, was apparently related to
   a. a genetic flaw which caused the corpus callosum to fail to develop
   b. a brain bisection early in his life
   c. the operation of cognitive dissonance
   d. the unique anatomy of P.S.'s visual system

13. Wernicke's area is important for
   a. speech production
   b. music comprehension
   c. speech comprehension
   d. music appreciation

14. Broca's aphasics exhibit impairment in   *Tom Broca = problem*
   a. speech production
   b. writing
   c. speech comprehension
   d. reading comprehension

15. In patients with bisected brains, the two cerebral hemispheres are disconnected by severing the
   a. planum temporale
   b. angular bundle
   c. sylvian fissure
   d. corpus callosum

True or False

_____ 1. Most of the neocortical area of humans is classified as association cortex and is not committed to sensation and movement.

_____ 2. While we are awake, our brains are constantly processing sensory information.

_____ 3. It has been known for a long time that in most people the left brain hemisphere controls language.

_____ 4. Following hemispherectomy, infants show more profound deficits than adults.

_____ 5. The neglect syndrome is seen following extensive damage to the posterior area of the right hemisphere.

_____ 6. We are not aware of the electrochemical processes within our brain that make consciousness possible.

_____ 7. Patients suffering from the neglect syndrome behave as if the left side of space had ceased to exist.

130

F 8. Severing of the corpus callosum in patients with intractable epilepsy results in sudden severe changes in personality, intelligence, and behavior.

T 9. Most people have a dominant eye, just as they have a dominant hand.

T 10. According to cognitive dissonance theory, humans feel a strong need to aviod disharmony between beliefs and actions.

F 11. Left-handedness is more common among the oriental cultures than is right-handedness, presumably due to the influence of their language upon brain development.

F 12. It is impossible to engage in complex sensory-motor acts, such as driving a car, without having engaged the conscious part of the mind.

F 13. Consciousness is a static process that remains relatively stable.

T 14. No studies have established the localization of musical abilities in one or the other hemisphere.

T 15. According to Roger Sperry, each hemisphere of the brain can be conceived of as having a "mind of its own."

Matching

g 1. planum temporale   a. damage to arcuate fasciculus

d 2. dyslexia   b. left visual cortex

i 3. Broca's aphasia   c. Japanese ideographic language

f 4. Wernicke's aphasia   d. more common in males

h 5. neglect syndrome   e. left hemisphere

a 6. conduction aphasia   f. impaired language comprehension

c 7. kanji   g. larger in the left hemisphere

j 8. Eran Zaidel   h. damage to right hemisphere

e 9. sequential processing   i. impaired speech

b 10. right visual field   j. Z lens

131

Short Answer

1. List some major functional differences in processing between the right and left hemispheres of the brain.

2. Define consciousness.

3. Describe the Wada test. What is this test for?

4. What is the dichotic listening test?

5. List and describe the two major types of aphasia.

ANSWERS TO SELF-TEST

Multiple Choice

1. a	2. b	3. a	4. c	5. d	6. a	7. b
8. a	9. d	10. c	11. d	12. b	13. c	14. a
15. d						

True or False

1. T	2. T	3. T	4. F	5. T	6. T	7. T
8. F	9. T	10. T	11. F	12. F	13. F	14. T
15. T						

Matching

1. g
2. d
3. i
4. f
5. h
6. a
7. c
8. j
9. e
10. b

CHAPTER 10
THE MALFUNCTIONING MIND

Before You Read This Chapter

OBJECTIVES

After reading this chapter, you should be able to do the following:

1. Understand the distinction between diseases of the brain and disorders of behavior.

2. Appreciate that disorders of brain and behavior are the result of brain-cell dysfunctions.

3. List the steps physicians employ in their diagnostic procedures when they see a patient with mental illness.

4. Describe the evidence suggesting that certain mental disorders are the result of inherited organic processes.

5. Define the Mental Status Examination and explain its use.

6. Explain how chemical tests are used as an adjunct to psychiatric diagnosis.

7. Distinguish among the affective psychoses: unipolar depression, mania, and the bipolar, or manic-depressive, psychoses.

8. Be able to describe the major degenerative diseases of the brain.

9. Describe the biological processes and environmental effects that play a role triggering mental illness.

10. Explain the catecholamine hypothesis of depression and its current status.

OUTLINE

Historical views of behavior disorders

Early descriptions
The last fifty years

133

Diseases of the brain and disorders of behavior

Brain-cell dysfunction
Diagnostic tests to identify brain disease

Normal versus abnormal variations in mood and thought

Degenerative diseases of the brain

Parkinson's disease
Huntington's disease
Alzheimer's disease

Diagnosis by analysis of behavior

The biological basis of psychosis

Clinical studies
Chemical studies

Affective psychosis

The nature of affective psychosis
Incidence of affective psychosis
Diagnosis of affective psychosis
The possible biological basis of affective psychosis
Other forms of treatment

The schizophrenias

The nature of the schizophrenias
Incidence of the schizophrenias
Basic types of schizophrenia
Biological clues to the nature of the schizophrenias
    The genetics of schizophrenia
    Biochemical hypotheses of schizophrenia
    Dopamine and schizophrenia

Brain, mind, and behavioral disorders: Future directions

THEME

In this chapter we investigate the biological basis of a number of common mental disorders. Long considered some of the most terrible afflictions to affect humans, the severe mental disorders known as the psychoses are particularly debilitating because they seriously interfere with thought processes. These diseases and disorders are relatively common in the population. Today many of these disorders can be treated and the symptoms alleviated, but for most of them the underlying biological defect remains unknown. This, however, is an area of intense research and rapidly advancing knowledge in the neurosciences, and it is widely anticipated that increased understanding of the biological basis of these disorders will some day result in more effective and definitive medical treatment.

This chapter does not attempt to exhaustively treat the whole gamut of mental illness. Rather, selected examples of mental illness are presented and their biological and environmental origins are considered. In keeping with the theme of this entire course, mental diseases (a diagnostic entity) and behavior disorders (a more general term for any condition of abnormality) are explained in terms of abnormal interactions between brain-cells. Many of the diseases of the brain are accompanied by a particular pathological condition in nervous tissue. The study of these organic diseases of the brain is generally the province of the neurologist. Other disorders of the brain are not represented by known organic or biological cellular dysfunctions and are termed functional disorders; these are generally the province of the psychiatrist or clinical psychologist. The distinction between organic and functional disorders does not imply that the functional disorder is without a biological basis. It most likely is. However, the biological basis of the functional disorder has not yet been discovered.

Diagnosis of Mental Illness

A physician who is confronted with a patient exhibiting mental illness will attempt to diagnose the disease or disorder. There are three steps involved in the diagnosis: obtaining a medical history of the patient, performing a thorough physical examination, and arranging for additional tests that may be necessary to identify the particular dysfunction. In some cases, however, even such a rigorous diagnostic procedure is not effective in precisely delimiting the nature of the brain or behavioral dysfunction. The disorders that we call diseases are those that display a consistent pattern of symptoms from individual to individual.

The textbook makes an important point when considering normal and abnormal variations in mood and thought. Virtually all of us have experienced periods of depression or elation, and some of us have experienced strange thoughts or impulses. The difference between the normal and abnormal individual, however, is that normal people retain control over their behavior and can consciously direct it, whereas abnormal or mentally ill individuals cannot. The behavior of individuals suffering from various forms of mental illness is generally controlled by the disease process. An interesting aspect of this subject is that, in a sense, abnormal behavior is defined within a statistical framework. In other words, normality is defined in terms of the predominant behavior expressed by a population; abnormality is behavior that deviates from the norm. You may wish to consider the controversial question of the normality of homosexual behavior in this regard. In years past, homosexual behavior was considered abnormal. Today, there is an increasing social acceptance of this alternative form of human sexual behavior. Does this mean that homosexuality should now be considered normal? You should reflect of the validity of these statistical arguments in terms of mental health.

Alzheimer's disease is a profound loss of memory functions, coupled with disorientation and, in advanced cases, depression, hallucinations, and delusions. Recent discoveries have shown that a nucleus at the base of the brain (the nucleus basalis) degenerates in the Alzheimer patient. The neurons in this nucleus release acetylcholine to widespread areas of the cerebral cortex and elsewhere. A potential treatment for Alzheimer's disease is the implantation of acetylcholine-secreting cells into critical regions of the brain to make up for the loss created by the disease process. While this is still an experimental technique, the idea of implanting other cells into specific regions of the brain is an exciting one for the future treatment of degenerative diseases--most of which seem to affect only certain populations of neurons in the brain. For example, Huntington's disease is associated with the degeneration of neurons specifically located in parts of the basal ganglia. This disease, as is suspected of many others, appears to have a strong genetic basis. The genetic involvement of Huntington's disease is such that the offspring of a patient will have a 50 percent chance of developing the disease. Since the disease does not appear until the victim is in the 30s or 40s, by this time he or she may have married and produced new carrier offspring. For patients afflicted with genetic disorders of this type, the development of diagnostic tests to identify which individuals are carriers of the disease would be a great benefit. They could refrain from passing on their defective genes to their offspring, possibly by adopting children rather than having their own. Ultimately, one would wish for a means of correcting the genetic fault in the afflicted individual to eradicate the disease itself. This, however, will only come about with increased understanding of the hereditary basis of the disease and the development of procedures to correct the problem.

One promising strategy that has been used with success in treating many forms of brain dysfunction is to identify the abnormal neurotransmitter system or systems in the brain. Once the affected neurotransmitter systems have been discovered, treatments can be devised to alleviate some of the symptoms of the disease, possibly with replacement therapy. Parkinson's disease, which is a dysfunction of motor modulatory systems brought about by degeneration of dopamine-transmitting cells in the substantia nigra, is a good example of this process. It has been treated by the administration of L-DOPA, which crosses the blood-brain barrier and is converted to dopamine. In all such discoveries, however, it is important to determine whether the changes seen are the causes of the disease or simply secondary effects of the disease process. This can be readily appreciated by a simple example. In the normal situation cell A, which contains dopamine, projects to cell B, which releases acetylcholine into other brain regions. Degeneration of A cells will then remove an important source of synaptic information for cell B, probably rendering its operation abnormal. If one only measured the consequences of the disease on cell B, one might erroneously conclude that an alteration in acetylcholine was the primary cause rather than understanding that this change was secondary to the loss of dopamine cells. Note, however, that in this example part of the disease may be represented by alterations both in dopamine and acetylcholine, and effective treatment may require manipulating both neurotransmitter systems.

Throughout this course we have emphasized the interaction that occurs between brain and environment. We have seen that many forms of environmental input are necessary for the proper development of brain circuitry. For example, the visual system requires visual input in order to develop to its fullest potential. Unfortunately, not all aspects of environmental input can be considered beneficial to the brain. There is growing suspicion that many of the substances produced by our "chemical society" may have toxic effects on the nervous system. For example, a correlation exists between the incidence of Parkinson's disease and living in an industrial environment, suggesting that a toxic chemical involved in industrial operations may be responsible for the degeneration of cells in the substantia nigra. The idea that specific chemicals may attack specific nuclei of the brain has been verified for certain viral infections. Today poliomyelitis is not regarded as a serious problem because of the development of effective vaccines. The polio virus shows a particular affinity for neurons in the spinal cord. It is suspected that other forms of viral infection, possibly some of the slow-developing ones, may be responsible for some varieties of brain disease and degeneration. Many slow viral infections have an extremely long time course, and years may pass before the disease is manifested.

Historical Views of Behavior Disorders

The textbook presents a brief review of the historical views of behavior disorders and the means by which mental patients were managed in the past. Most early thought regarding mental illness reflects its society and the assumptions of the time. Early societies considered behavioral disorders as evil spirits that had taken possession of the afflicted individuals and often resorted to punishment or exorcism. Many of the early behavioral disorders were of an organic nature and were caused by dietary deficiencies or unrecognized genetic faults. An example of a diet-based disorder is pellagra, a disease caused by an insufficiency of niacin, a B vitamin. Pellagra is often associated with delirium, confusion, and generalized disorientation of the victim. Once the necessity for this vitamin in the diet was recognized, the administration of adequate levels of the vitamin totally eliminated this form of mental illness. If the terms "organic" and "functional" had been in use then, pellagra undoubtedly would have been considered a functional disorder, since the biological cause was as yet unknown. As soon as the organic cause of the disease became known, it could be managed effectively. Today many scientists believe that a similar situation exists for some of the functional disorders that currently affect humans. As soon as the organic basis of these diseases is understood, effective treatment will probably be forthcoming.

A historical example of a genetic abnormality leading to mental illness is seen in the case of King George III of England (the "mad king"), who suffered from the inheritable metabolic disease currently known as acute intermittent porphyria. This disease results in neurological disturbances (i.e., fluctuating cycles of apparent insanity and normality) and is due to genetically defective hemoglobin molecules. This is another example of an organic mental illness. The affliction of George III gave impetus to the scientific study of mental illness. Because of his importance, programs were begun in his time to research the disease processes. Today there are also special programs sponsored by research foundations and government agencies to aid afflicted groups with enough political persuasion to create these programs. Thus "patrons" to further particular research efforts have been employed historically in the sciences as well as in the arts.

Diseases of the Brain

The textbook provides a third example of organic mental illness-- general paresis, which is a late stage in the brain infection known as neurosyphilis. Neurosyphilis is the result of a bacterial infection of the brain and can be cured today by antibiotic medication. It is thought by many that some of the functional mental disorders may, in fact, be organically based in other forms of brain infection, perhaps involving slow-growing viruses or other such agents that have recently been discovered. As more information is gained about the nature of these slow viral infections, many of which can take years to manifest themselves, we can anticipate the advent of effective treatment for these diseases.

The Mental Status Examination

Once organic brain disease has been ruled out, the physician is left with an array of behavioral symptoms from which a functional diagnosis must be made. The diagnosis is accomplished in part by means of a physician-patient interview, which is called the Mental Status Examination. Seven areas of mental and emotional function are investigated in the Mental Status Examination:

1. consciousness
2. affective emotional tone
3. motor behavior
4. thinking
5. perception
6. memory
7. intelligence

The textbook describes some of the features that are looked for under each of these categories. By conducting a Mental Status Examination, it is often possible to diagnose the disease that is affecting the patient. Historically, one of the barriers to the effective diagnosis of functional disorders has been the subjective nature of the diagnosis. In recent years significant advances have been made in making the diagnostic process and categories uniform. This is an essential first step in attempting to understand the basis of these functional disorders.

Biological Basis of Psychosis

Considerable research is currently being done into the biological basis of many of the more severe functional disorders, termed the psychoses. One of the great obstacles to research in this area is the lack of suitable animals that display behavioral symptoms similar to those displayed by human beings. Many of the "tools of the trade" of modern neuroscience involve invasive techniques that cannot be performed on living humans. With that in mind, it is perhaps easier to understand why clinical studies have gained such importance in understanding psychotic disorders. Studies that have examined the degree to which mental illness is passed on from generation to generation have shown that some diseases are quite definitely inherited, since the incidence rate within the family line far exceeds that for the rest of the population.

One of the most effective experimental approaches to disentangling the role of genetic factors versus environmental factors has been twin studies. Twin studies can help us investigate the possibility that the mental illness seen in a family line may be the result of specific environmental factors that are passed down culturally from generation to generation. If such environmental factors exist, then it is impossible to assert that the effects are being transmitted genetically as opposed to culturally. Studies employing twins have proved quite useful in understanding the relative contributions of genetics and environment to mental illness. Identical twins share the same fertilized egg and are totally identical genetically. Researchers have painstakingly sought out twins who were adopted after birth and thereby removed from an environment or cultural influence in their family line. These studies have documented the existence of an inheritable factor in certain disorders such as schizophrenia; however, a genetic explanation alone is never enough to account for all of the observed illnesses. At present the most likely explanation of these results is that the genetic inheritance provides a "predisposition" to schizophrenia but that an environmental stimulus is necessary to trigger the disease.

The development of the field of psychopharmacology in the 1950s led to a revolution in the treatment of mental patients in this country and around the world. A number of effective drugs were developed for treating schizophrenia and other forms of mental illness. Dopamine, which is a neurotransmitter involved in schizophrenia, is blocked by these drugs, which do not cure mental illness but do alleviate many of the thought disorders associated with schizophrenia. The net effect of the widespread use of these drugs has been to sharply reduce the number of mental patients hospitalized in this country. Many of these patients, as long as they maintain their medication, are able to resume useful places in society or at least be cared for in community-based treatment facilities. Although this advance has been salutory, it has had some negative repercussions. A side-effect of the long-term use of these drugs has been the development of a disease known as tardive dyskinesia, which is a motor disturbance very much like Parkinson's disease. Another unfortunate result of this revolution in the treatment of mental patients in this country is that some of the previously hospitalized patients no longer receive the institutional support they need and are to be found in the flop houses, public shelters, sidewalks, and soup kitchens of America's cities.

The Schizophrenias

The schizophrenia psychoses are a collection of severe thought disorders that are typified by the victim's having altered perceptual, emotional, and thought processes. Several examples of disordered mental processes associated with schizophrenia are presented in the text. While schizophrenics can display varied symptoms and have been subclassified into a number of groups, all exhibit disturbed thought processes, and in many the disease takes an episodic form--it comes and goes over extended periods of time. About half the admissions to mental hospitals are schizophrenic patients. This is a major health problem in this country, as the disease has a high incidence in the general population. Schizophrenia used to be called "dementia praecox" because its time of onset was common among people between the ages of 20 and 30 years. Schizophrenia can be a life-long illness, and the patient may suffer bouts of abnormal behavior interspersed with relatively normal periods. Recently attention has been focused on two basic forms of schizophrenia, termed type I and type II. The distinction between the two forms relates to their symptoms and to the drugs that are most useful in treating each one. Since the two forms of the illness are quite different, and since only type-II schizophrenia shows pathological changes in the brain, it is believed that two different biological processes underlie these two forms of the illness. As mentioned earlier, there seems to be a strong genetic component in the incidence of schizophrenia, with documented schizophrenic episodes occurring along family lines.

The biological basis of schizophrenia is currently under intense investigation. Since drugs that are effective in treating schizophrenic patients appear to act by modulating dopamine synaptic transmission and since some drugs that can produce some of the symptoms of schizophrenia act at synaptic transmission sites, it appears as if the locus of the defect is within the synaptic chemistry of the brain. While a good deal of evidence points to some defect in dopamine transmission, there are many findings that do not fit the interpretation that dopamine is the critical transmitter system at fault in schizophrenia.

Affective Disorders

The other major psychoses discussed in this chapter are the affective psychoses. These disorders are typified by an alteration in mood. Most normal individuals have mood swings in which they are elated or depressed, but generally one can find an environmental situation that is related to the change. Not so in the case of the individual who is afflicted with affective psychosis; these individuals may experience intense sadness and grief or remarkable elation and euphoria that often cannot be attributed to any environmental event.

There are three major types of affective disorders: unipolar depression, mania, and bipolar psychosis. A patient suffering from unipolar depression shows only periodic depressive symptoms; a patient suffering from mania displays periodic euphoria; and a patient suffering from bipolar, or manic-depressive psychosis, is alternately depressed or manic. The incidence of affective psychosis is quite high; about one out of every four adults experiences some form of severe affective disorder at some time during his or her life.

The biological defect underlying the affective disorders is unknown. What is known is that treatment with drugs that have been found to alter the brain's concentration of the monoamine transmitters norepinephrine, serotonin, and dopamine, is effective in controlling these disorders. Observations of the role of the catecholamines (norepinephrine and dopamine) led to the development of the catecholamine hypothesis, in which the affective disorders were explained by loss of transmission at the catecholamine synapses in sensitive brain regions. The student may want to review the basic chemistry of synaptic transmission presented in Chapter 2 as an aid to understanding the logic behind the catecholamine hypothesis. However, as is the case with dopamine involvement in schizophrenia, experimental tests of the involvement of catecholamines in affective disorders have not provided definitive proof.

At our present stage of understanding of these disorders, we are faced with many tantalizing clues and much conflicting evidence regarding the biological basis of mental illness. While we cannot pinpoint the biological mechanism that has gone awry in these conditions, there is a general feeling among neuroscientists that such advances will be forthcoming, given our increasingly rapid accumulation of knowledge regarding the function of the normal and abnormal brain.

The Dysfunctional Brain

We have examined several of the major forms of mental illness that afflict humans. We have seen that it is possible to class these disorders into two categories, organic and functional. Organic disorders are those for which it is possible to identify a biological cause. Functional disorders are those for which there is no known biological cause. The history of our knowledge of mental illness indicates that as more and more is known about the biology of the brain, more diseases will be reclassified from functional to organic.

The diagnosis of mental illness can be a difficult process, particularly for functional disorders that display a wide spectrum of symptoms in different individuals. In all such diagnostic procedures, three important steps are followed. First, a detailed medical history of the patient is obtained; second, a medical examination is performed to rule out physical causes of the illness; and third, additional specialized tests are given to pinpoint the disease process. The diagnosis of functional disorders is made more complex because there is no know biological cause, and we are forced to rely upon a detailed behavioral examination--the Mental Status Examination. The importance of uniform and consistent diagnosis was emphasized as a first step in understanding and treating disease in a scientific manner.

Since all individuals periodically display some forms of aberrant mental behavior, from euphoria to thought disorders, the question arises as to the precise definition of normal versus abnormal behavior. The primary difference is that the normal individual retains control over his or her own thought processes, whereas the sick individual is at the mercy of the aberrant thought processes and cannot bring them under control.

We have seen that the early treatment of individuals suffering from mental illness was based on quite different assumptions from ours. Before being too critical of our ancestors, however, we should understand that in the centuries preceding ours medical knowledge was relatively limited. Over the years, the question of the role of the environment in mental illness has been widely debated. Recent investigations have tended to support the notion that certain forms of mental illness, such as schizophrenia, possess a significant genetic component, which, when combined with unspecified but deleterious environmental conditions, will trigger mental illness in the genetically predisposed individual.

The drug treatments that are effective in alleviating the symptoms of the major psychoses interact with brain transmitter systems, particularly with dopamine, norepinephrine, and serotonin. The limited success of such drugs has led to several hypotheses implicating deficiencies in these neurotransmitter systems as the biological bases for the illnesses. Most of these hypotheses have not withstood the rigor of additional scientific investigations, however, and they are currently being questioned.

The most prevalent of the major psychoses are the affective disorders, consisting of unipolar depression, mania, and bipolar psychoses. Afflicting one out of every four individuals, these psychotic episodes are manifested in the form of mood swings on the part of the afflicted individual. The affective disorders appear to respond best to drugs that interact with the catecholamine family of neurotransmitters.

Mental illness remains a frontier area of the neurosciences, and one in which rapid advances are expected to occur in the years to come. It is anticipated that the cellular basis of these disorders will yield to scientific inquiry, resulting in the development of more effective treatments.

QUESTIONS TO KEEP IN MIND AS YOU READ THE CHAPTER

1. One often hears people make reference to "nervous breakdowns." To what are these individuals referring?

2. Given the range of behaviors that exist among people, how is it possible to define what is normal?

3. How can environmental stressors apparently trigger emotional illness in some individuals and not in others?

4. The foundation of some varieties of psychotherapy relies upon in-depth probing of an individual's past and present motivations. How effective do you think these techniques would be for the individual suffering from schizophrenia or from a manic-depressive psychosis?

5. Given the emerging knowledge that some forms of mental illness, particularly schizophrenia, appear to run in families, what would be your personal response to bringing children into the world if your family had a history of schizophrenia?

6. The history of our treatment of those afflicted with mental disorders reveals a marked lack of enlightenment and understanding. Do you feel that historians of the future will look back to the present era and make the same comments about the way we handle mental illness?

7. What are the differences between senescence and degenerative brain diseases?

8. What treatments are useful in treating the degenerative diseases?

After You Have Read This Chapter, Continue with the Following Material

STUDENT'S OUTLINE

After you have read this chapter and studied the material it contains, close the book and in the space below, using your own words, try to outline the major points that you have just read. The basic structure of the chapter is provided below.

Historical views of behavior disorders

Diseases of the brain and disorders of behavior

Normal versus abnormal variations in mood and thought

Degenerative diseases of the brain

Diagnosis by analysis of behavior

The biological basis of psychosis

Affective psychosis

The schizophrenias

Brain, mind, and behavioral disorders: Future directions

Now that you have attempted to outline this chapter from memory, go back to the textbook and see how accurate your recollection was. Fill in those topics you might have missed and emphasize the points that are stressed in the textbook.

Key Terms

The following terms were introduced in this chapter. You should be sure that these terms are familiar to you and that you have their definitions well in hand.

Affective psychoses
Alzheimer's disease
Anxiety
Atherosclerosis
Bipolar depression (manic-depressive psychosis)
Catecholamine hypothesis of depression
Dementia
Dexamethasone supression test
Dopamine

Down syndrome
Huntington's disease
Mania
Manic-depressive psychosis
Neurofibrillary tangles
Neurology
Neurosis
Obsessive-compulsive behavior
Pathology
Pellagra
Porphyria
Positron emission tomography
Psychoses
Schizophrenia
Senile plaques
Unipolar depression

SELF-TEST

Multiple-Choice

1. The first mental "asylums" were established by
   a. the Chinese
   b. the ancient Greeks
   c. the American government
   d. Arab physicians

2. Weyer and Paracelsus were the first to express the view that
   a. mental illness is communicable
   b. mental illness affects the soul
   c. mental illness may reflect a medical problem
   d. mental illness is genetically based

3. General paresis, a mental disorder produced by untreated syphilis, was at one time cured by
   a. quinine treatment
   b. malaria infection
   c. removal of the diseased tissue
   d. corn niacin supplements

4. In the U.S., annual suicides directly attributable to affective psychosis number
   a. less than 1000
   b. 1000 to 5000
   c. 5000 to 10,000
   d. over 20,000

5. Generally, antipsychotic drugs are most effective in patients displaying
   a. Type I schizophrenia
   b. Type II schizophrenia
   c. Type III schizophrenia
   d. negative symptoms

6. Frequent thought and motor problems, weight loss, and short REM latency are characteristics of
   a. psychomotor depression
   b. neurotic depression
   c. psychotic depression
   d. ineffective depression

7. Reserpine has been shown to deplete the brain's content of
   a. glutamine
   b. amphetamines
   c. monoamines
   d. none of the above

8. In persons over the age of 55, the incidence of schizophrenia is estimated to be 1 in
   a. 10
   b. 100
   c. 500
   d. 1000

9. The "negative symptoms" of schizophrenia include
   a. hallucinations
   b. thought disorders
   c. delusions
   d. motivational disorders

10. The English psychiatrist Crow has suggested the separation of schizophrenia into two major classes:
    a. unipolar and bipolar
    b. psychotic and neurotic
    c. Type I and type II
    d. bacterial and viral

11. Acute psychotic episodes induced in patients with Parkinson's disease by L-DOPA overdose support the contention that
    a. Parkinson's disease reflects an underlying dopamine disorder
    b. dopamine metabolism is disturbed in schizophrenia
    c. dopamine enhancers should be effective antipsychotic drugs
    d. L-DOPA treatment should be discontinued

12. Neuroleptic drugs are
    a. antipsychotics
    b. antidepressants
    c. antileprosy
    d. none of the above

13. The most prevalent psychiatric disease is
    a. schizophrenia
    b. pellegra
    c. general paresis
    d. affective psychosis

14. Type I schizophrenics
    a. often show shrinkage of neural tissue
    b. are characterized by negative symptoms
    c. are treated with MAO inhibitors
    d. none of the above

15. The most common chemical dependency involves
    a. alcohol
    b. barbiturates
    c. chocolate
    d. cocaine

True or False

_____ 1. "Functional" disorders are the same as "organic" disorders.

_____ 2. Huntington's disease has been shown to be an autosomal dominant disorder.

_____ 3. Abnormal states of behavior were first recorded in the middle ages.

_____ 4. Corn niacin is utilized in the treatment of pellegra.

_____ 5. Untreated syphllis was once a major cause of mental illness.

_____ 6. Mental illness cannot be induced by bacterial infection.

_____ 7. Drug treatments are always successful in cases of schizophrenia and affective psychoses.

_____ 8. Fraternal twins demonstrate a higher likelihood that both twins will exhibit schizophrenia than do identical twins.

_____ 9. Problems with sleeping and eating are often associated with affective psychoses.

_____ 10. Suicides directly attributable to affective psychosis are rare.

_____ 11. Depressed patients who enter their first REM period quickly are good candidates for antidepressant drug treatment.

_____ 12. Schizophrenic patients do not demonstrate periods of normal behavior.

_____ 13. In the U.S., more than 300,000 new cases of schizophrenia are diagnosed every year.

_____ 14. The interpretations from twin research have been questioned because twins as a group demonstrate a higher incidence of schizophrenia than the average population.

_F_ 15. Reserpine treatment studies strongly support the catecholamine hypothesis of depression.

Matching

_C_ 1. Schildkraut and Kety   a. disorder of the basal ganglia

_e_ 2. Parkinson's disease   b. overall emotional state

_a_ 3. Huntington's disease   c. catecholamine hypothesis of depression

_h_ 4. Alzheimer's disease   d. porphyria

_d_ 5. King George III   e. treatment with L-DOPA

_f_ 6. "positive" symptom of schizophrenia   f. hallucinations

_i_ 7. "negative" symptom of schizophrenia   g. niacin (B vitamin) deficit

_B_ 8. affect   h. genetic link to Down syndrome

_J_ 9. mania   i. decreased spontaneous speech

_G_ 10. pellagra   j. form of affective psychosis

Short Answer

1. Define the term "diseased mind" in one hundred words or less.

2. To what does "organic" in the term organic brain disease refer?

3. Name four diagnostic tools available to a neurologist for studying disordered brain function.

4. What evidence suggests that a biological basis exists for the major psychiatric diseases?

5. Discuss several possible explanations for the high incidence of schizophrenia found in several circumscribed geographical locations.

ANSWERS TO SELF-TEST

Multiple Choice

1. d	2. c	3. b	4. d	5. a	6. c	7. c
8. b	9. d	10. c	11. b	12. a	13. d	14. d
15. a						

True or False

1. F	2. T	3. F	4. F	5. T	6. F	7. F
8. F	9. T	10. F	11. T	12. F	13. T	14. F
15. F						

Matching

1. c
2. e
3. a
4. h
5. d
6. f
7. i
8. b
9. j
10. g

TELECOURSE USERS GUIDE

Introduction

THE BRAIN is an eight-part televcourse series produced by WNET in New York for the Public Broadcasting System. The programs of THE BRAIN telecourse convey the essence of modern brain research and its bearing on our knowledge of human psychology.

This Telecourse Users Guide is designed to be used with the television programs, the textbook and the preceeding chapters of the Study Guide.

How to Use the Television Programs

Television courses like THE BRAIN telecourse are somewhat different from traditional courses. These courses are designed for people who find it more convenient to fit their studying into their own busy, personal schedules. Many will appreciate the opportunity to watch the programs and study at home without having to travel to a campus.

Since television coursework may be new to you, the following suggestions about how to maximize the benefits from this form of education may be useful.

1. Be sure that you obtain copies of the textbook and this Study Guide for your own use. Do not try to take this telecourse without them. The television programs are not intended to be exhaustive in their treatment of the subject matter, whereas the books are.

2. Watch all the television programs. Much of the material presented on the television is included because it can be communicated in a more effective manner than by the printed word. Many students find that writing down key words during the program will help them make more detailed notes at the end of the program.

If you miss a program, don't despair. Many stations repeat these programs at a later date, and often your college may have copies of the programs available for viewing in the library. Call upon your faculty person for assistance--that is what he or she is for.

3. Keep up with the assignments. It is easy to let things slide, particularly if you do not have any class sessions or assignments to turn in. But if you do fall behind, you will find that it is very diffucult to catch up. This Study Guide was written to assist you in mastering the material and provides assignments for you to do *before* reading the material and viewing the program, and excercises for you to do afterward.

4. Get to know your faculty member for this telecourse. The instructor can help you with questions or problems related to the course content, missed lessons, or additional information and examinations and he or she would very much like to hear from you regarding your experiences during this telecourse.

READING ASSIGNMENTS

Program 1 *The Enlightened Machine*
   Ch. 1 Introduction to the Nervous System
   Ch. 2 The Cellular Machinery of the Brain
   Ch. 3 Development of the Brain through the Lifespan

Program 2 *Vision and Movement*
   Ch. 4 Sensing and Moving

Program 3 *Rhythms and Drives*
   Ch. 5 Homeostasis: Maintaining the Internal Environment
   Ch. 6 Rhythms of the Brain

Program 4 *Stress and Emotion*
   Ch. 7 Emotions: The Highs and Lows of the Brain

Program 5 *Learning and Memory*
   Ch. 8 Learning and Memory

Program 6 *The Two Brains*
   Ch. 9 Thinking and Consciousness

Program 7 *Madness*
   Ch. 10 The Malfunctioning Mind

Program 8 *The Brain Age*

PROGRAM 1: THE ENLIGHTENED MACHINE

Introduction

For some of you this course represents a journey into new territory--
territory that may appear unrecognizable and unknowable. As you will
learn, however, the brain is beginning to share its mysteries. As
participants in this course, you will be witnesses to the excitement
that is represented by the neurosciences.

In the opening scenes of this first program you will see pictures
of an alien landscape: masses of cables, large boulder-like objects
strewn about, an incredible amount of detail compressed into a tiny
space. These are scenes from inside the brain as is seen by a scanning electron microscope. Out of this seemingly impenetrable jungle
of brain matter comes everything that makes us human--thought,
feeling, memories, sensation, motion.

Brain Function

How does the brain work? This question has intrigued scientists and
laymen alike. In the program we see some of the pioneers in thinking
about how the brain works. Many of the early conceptions of brain
function are today rejected and sometimes looked upon with amusement.
We should be cautious, however, in laughing at our predecessors for
they, just as we, were attempting to explain how the brain works based
on the information available to them. Perhaps in several centuries
future scientists will look back on our own activities with a good
deal of amusement. Time will tell.

In an attempt to understand the operations of the human brain
people have drawn metaphors to the "high-tech" developments of their
time: the telegraph, the telephone, the computer. This is still
being done today with metaphors being drawn to parallel processing
computers and hologram information storage devices. But do these
analogies really help us understand how the brain works?

In the first program we see a racecar driver navigating the
corners, accelerating, utilizing his sensory apparatus, his analytical
powers, in a goal-directed manner attempting to go ever faster, utilizing muscle systems to control the speeding race car. How is it that
a seemingly frail assemblage of neurons can control so many functions
in such an integrated way so rapidly? While we do not have complete
answers to this question we are beginning to see how the brain can
orchestrate such things. The images of the working brain of the race
car driver will be expanded on in succeeding programs to provide
details and analyze what is known about the operation of these various
brain systems and how they interact with one another.

Tools to Study the Brain

Today the neurosciences are witnessing a revolution partly brought about by the advent of new technology which allows us to study the brain in ways heretofore not possible. The EEG machine is probably familiar to most as it has been employed for years to record the electrical activity from the surface of the scalp. Familiar to many will be the CAT scan. Computerized axial tomography (CAT) is a sophisticated X-ray machine which allows the reconstruction of the three-dimensional views inside the patient's head and body. CAT scans allow the researcher access to the forbidden interior of the human brain and offer the physician a way of detecting abnormalities, such as tumors, inside the brain. PETT scans are a more recent development. Positron emission transaxial tomography (PETT) utilizes radioactively labeled substances that are introduced into the brain. These substances can be used to reflect some aspect of the biochemistry of the nervous system. PETT scans allow one to view the operation, not just the anatomy, of the human brain. It is almost as if a chemical probe were magically inserted into the brain to simultaneously detect the activity throughout the brain. Newer still, we see the advent of the EEG topographic map. In this sophisticated extension of the EEG, it is possible to watch the distribution of electrical activity as it changes dramatically across the surface of the skull. Using the EEG topographic map one can monitor brain activity in widespread locations as it is occurring.

These are some of today's tools for exploring the brain. Tomorrow brings the promise of new and more powerful tools that will open windows into the brain that have not previously existed. Their use will provide researcher and physician alike with valuable information regarding the operation of the normal and abnormal brain.

Epilepsy

In the person of young Jason Reyes we see one kind of brain dysfunction that can afflict an individual. Jason suffers from epilepsy which is characterized by "electrical storms" in the nervous system. During an epileptic seizure, the brain loses control and seizures result. We see in this segment that epilepsy represents a medical problem for the treating physician--but a medical problem that usually responds well to drug therapy. Epilepsy also represents a personal problem for the afflicted individual--the seizures are potentially dangerous, are psychologically destructive, and are associated with a social stigma. In Jason we see a mature ten-year old who accepts his medical problem with dignity, although he hates taking his medications, partly because of the side effects that he has experienced in the past. We also see that epilepsy represents a family problem--Jason's parents are very supportive and are adept at coping with the problems associated with the management of this disease on a medical and personal level. Nevertheless, brain diseases like epilepsy can take their toll on friends and family.

A key to understanding the brain dysfunction underlying epilepsy, and the key to understanding many other forms of brain dysfunction, lies in understanding the synaptic basis of communication between neurons. Throughout this course we shall be emphasizing the

153

importance of understanding which neurotransmitters and which neural systems are involved in both brain disorders and in normal functions. It is an important key to understanding the operation of the brain.

A great deal can be learned about the brain by observing behavior. The brain is the ultimate organ of behavior. By looking at behavior we can often infer brain dysfunctions. In the program we see Dr. Fred Plum with a group of young residents as they observe the abnormal behaviors of patients afflicted with a variety of brain disorders. We see not only the counsel that a wise physician imparts to young residents, but the importance of analyzing behavior in an objective way, as another of the windows into the brain.

Understanding Brain Function

There are a number of critical themes that help one understand brain function. As explained by Dr. Eric Kandel, who traces the history of brain science through the work of such men as Gall, Florens, Broca, Wernicke, and Ramon y Cajal, at least three themes are important in understanding brain function. The first is that the inaccessibility of the human brain and its overwhelming complexity forces the scientist to employ animal models which can be studied in the laboratory. The animal brains chosen for study are considerably simpler and thus more amenable to analysis than is the human brain. The second theme is: What structures in the brain are responsible for which phenomena? Once a function and a structure can be paired, a large impediment to progress in understanding the brain has been surmounted. The third major theme is the overwhelming importance of the neuron. The elementary component of the brain, the neuron is an exquisitely complicated processing unit. The human brain contains more than 200 billion neurons connected in complex ways. The neuron is the key to understanding virtually every aspect of brain function. We shall encounter these three themes throughout this course: animal models, localization of function, and neuron function.

Huntington's Disease

The brain works at the interface between genetics and environment. Occasionally, environmental conditions can trigger brain disease and occasionally genetic errors can be the cause of brain dysfunction. In Huntington's disease we see that there are strong genetic components to this disorder, as documented by Dr. Wexler in her studies of a particularly afflicted community in Venezuela. Many diseases can be influenced, controlled, and even reversed as a function of brain processes. Many examples exist of patients "willing" themselves to recover from serious disease, whereas others apparently "will" themselves to die when their loved ones have passed on.

Stroke

Many of the things that the brain is capable of doing remain a complete mystery. In the last segments of the program we see a child suffering from hydrocephalus. Nevertheless this child displays normal function. How can this individual appear normal while lacking so much brain tissue? We do not know. We observe the dancer Agnes DeMille, who suffered a crippling stroke. Faced with her remarkable recovery, one is left with the question, how can this recovery occur? Again, we do not know. How much of the brain's self-healing abilities are due to a person's will? The answer is again--we do not know.

In this program we have touched upon themes that will permeate the rest of this series. The idea that the understanding of the brain as a biological organ will ultimately lead us to understand all of these phenomena is central to this series. At the conclusion of this course, it is hoped that you will have gained a considerable degree of knowledge about our current understanding of brain structure and function and its relationship to behavior and will appreciate the future challenges left for the neurosciences to uncover.

Enjoy and learn!

-Timothy J. Teyler, Ph.D.

PROGRAM 2: VISION AND MOVEMENT

Introduction

We see the remarkable athletic performance of Greg Louganis, an Olympic highdiver, and are impressed with the considerable abilities that he demonstrates. Not to deny the remarkable achievements of Greg Louganis, our everyday activities represent equally as remarkable accomplishments. Reflect on what is occurring in your brain as you walk down the street, ride a bicycle, or engage in an athletic activity. Brain circuits must be active, allowing you to avoid obstacles, maintain your desired objectives, subtly adjust your musculature to maintain balance, be alert to unexpected happenings and coordinate all of the body musculature into a smooth-flowing movement. The relatively simple acts of walking, riding, and playing require a considerable degree of brain processing. Currently scientists in a number of laboratories are attempting to devise interfaces between computers and paralyzed individuals to allow them to walk again. The limited success of efforts today point out the incredible demands that are placed upon the brain to accomplish such simple phenomena as walking down the street. In this program we investigate the capabilities of one of the sensory systems--vision--and look at what is involved in movement.

Vision

If someone told you that you could "see" with your back, you would probably think them crazy. Nevertheless, as is documented in this program, a blind person, given appropriate experience, can "see" by means of a tactile stimulators vibrating on his back which convey the tactile equivalent of a visual image. Clearly the act of "seeing" does not require eyes. The important aspect in seeing is that the perceptual judgment regarding the meaning of the sensory event is understood whether it is in verbal form, printed form, or, in the case of Braille, read through the fingertips. What are the brain mechanism that allow such phenomena as vision and the perception of visual objects to occur? Clearly there is no one inside your head looking at the pictures that are represented on your retina and on your cortex. How then does it occur?

Does the visual system work like a camera? Are images recorded on the brain as they are recorded on film? We are shown the results of an experiment by Dr. Russell DeValois using a metabolic mapping technique who showed a faithful representation of the visual object on the surface of the visual cortex. So in some senses, it is possible to think of the brain as representing a faithful reproduction of visual objects on the brain.

How does the brain manage to recreate and represent sensory images in terms of brain structure and function? We see from the work of Drs. Hubel and Wiesel that lines, bars, edges, and contrast are encoded by single neurons of the visual cortex. These, according to Drs. Hubel and Wiesel, are the raw elements of all images. Not all scientists agree with such a conclusion. As Dr. DeValois points out, many of the visual images that confront us daily are smooth gradations and flowing contours rather than lines, bars, and edges. Dr. DeValois emphasizes instead the role of frequencies of visual information as they gradually change across the visual field. Dr. Hubel, on the other hand, stresses that the role of primary visual cortex is to detect and extract contours and that such a process can explain much, if not all, of vision. As is true in many controversies considerable truth may lie with each vantage point. Only with the accumulation of additional knowledge regarding the operation of the visual system will we be able to specify in precise detail the mechanism utilized by the visual system to extract information from the world.

Visual plasticity

It has been known for a long time that the brain is capable of changing its own function to allow the operation of such phenomena as learning and memory. However, the experiment that is duplicated in this program is a remarkable and surprising demonstration of incredible properties of the brain. We see Suzanna, a student in France, who has agreed to wear special glasses that flip the visual world upside down. As you can imagine, and as is shown in the program, the experience of an upside-down world is totally disruptive and such simple acts as pouring tea into a cup become laughingly difficult. However, after a few days the world no longer appears upside down and Suzanna has no difficulty in navigating through space and even riding a bicycle. After wearing the inverting glasses for a week, however, when they are taken off the world again flips and she again experiences a brief period of disorientation. What has happened in the brain? Suzanna's perception of the upside-down world gradually came to be regarded as normal. We can only imagine what kinds of reorganizations must have occurred in Suzanna's visual cortex.

Higher-order visual processing

The brain's analysis of visual images does not stop with the extraction of lines, bars, edges, and contours; rather, it continues on to the perception of objects and their spatial relations. We see in the work of Dr. Mortimer Mishkin that there are two areas beyond the visual cortex that are concerned with these higher-order extractions of visual information. One region in the parietal cortex of the brain is concerned with the spatial location of objects in the visual field, an important aspect in our navigation through space and maintaining our perspective in a three-dimensional world. The second area, located at the bottom of the temporal lobe, is concerned with object analysis and recognition. Here we find cells that respond preferentially to such complicated objects as drawings of the face of the experimental monkey. Does this imply that the brain is filled with individual cells whose function it is to identify and respond to individual faces and other objects? The consensus of current scientific thought is that these cells represent the cumulative result of extensive feature extraction by other cells "upstream." As you might expect, damage to this area of the brain leads to an inability in recognizing faces and other objects. Still beyond this region of the brain other circuits take the process of visual analysis deep into the brain where the hippocampus and amygdala may analyze the visual information in terms of memory and emotionality.

Motor patterns

How is Greg Louganis capable of becoming such a proficient diver? How do any of us become proficient at everyday motor skills? Such abilities depend upon the brain's establishing a "highway" or effective link between the involved brain regions. Thus we see in Greg Louganis the end result of the neurobiology of athletic practice, setting down an almost reflexive pattern of motor behaviors forged into existence by continued practice and feedback.

How are such motor behaviors capable of being learned? Dr. Rudolfo Llinas studies nerve-muscle interaction in the squid. He finds that there are few differences between the simple neurocircuitry of the human in terms of their fundamental operations. The basic processes are the same, but the control of motor behavior is handled by a complex net of millions of cells rather than by the relatively few of the squid. The result is more flexibility, adaptability, and plasticity.

Parkinson's Disease

Movements do not exist in isolation. They occur embedded in patterns of whole body motor activity. Coordination is the hallmark of a successful athlete and is accomplished by means of two brain regions, the cerebellum and the basal ganglia. These brain regions contain motor programs which, when well learned, can unreel under command from higher motor centers in the motor cortex. Disorders of the cerebellum and the basal ganglia result in disturbances of movement. We see in the actor Terry Thomas the effect of one such disease--Parkinson's disease. In Parkinson's disease cells of the substantia nigra die. These cells, which contain the neurotransmitter dopamine, project to the basal ganglia and are important components in the regulation of motor behavior. Without the dopamine supplied by substantia nigra cells, the victim experiences difficulty initiating movements and exhibits a pronounced tremor of the hand and other muscles. As Terry Thomas says "it's as though one's feet are glued to the floor". In advanced stages, walking itself is almost impossible without aid. Treatment with the biochemical precusor to dopamine, L-DOPA, is rapid and dramatic.

We see in the last segment of this program hope for treating Parkinson's disease and other degenerative diseases of the nervous system. The day may come when tissue implants may be an answer. Research in Sweden shows that dopamine-producing cells from the adrenal gland may be an effective treating for alleviating the problems due to the lack of dopamine caused by cell death in Parkinson's disease. All of these medical advances are worked out in painstaking animal experiments often requiring years to yield answers. Without the ability to take advantage of the similarity between the human and

158

animal brain, most of the medical advances that we have benefited from, not only in the neurosciences but elsewhere, would have been impossible.

In Chapter 4 we learn more about the visual and motor systems of the brain and appreciate the commonalties between all the senses. Concentrating on the visual system, the chapter considers the biological basis of many aspects of vision such as color vision, depth perception and the feature extracting properties of visual neurons. The biology of the brain's motor systems is explored in depth, focusing upon circuits in the motor cortex, basal ganglia, and cerebellum.

PROGRAM 3: RHYTHMS AND DRIVES

Introduction

In this program we explore some of the more basic manifestations of the human brain. Many of the phenomena covered in this program are seen not only in human brains, but also in the brains of animals. If one could remove the cortex of a human brain, the rest of the brain would be rather similar to that possessed by many other animal species. That is to say, that the essential portions of the brain thought to convey humanity to humans reside in the cortex. In this program we examine primarily the manifestations of subcortical activity. We explore emotionality, the rhythms of the body and brain, aggression and violence, and sexual behavior.

Winter Depression

For many people living through long winters, it is a time of the "blahs" and a yearning for fresh spring breezes. For some, however, the manifestations of winter can be much more severe. We see Pat Moore, a woman suffering from severe "winter depression." In a remarkable scientific discovery, Pat Moore's problem was found to be related to the lack of sunlight that she experienced during the winter. A nucleus deep in the brain, a part of the hypothalamus called the suprachiasmatic nucleus, receives information from the eyes regarding the day/night cycle. In winter there is, of course, considerably less daylight than in summer. The effect of this relative lack of light on the suprachiasmatic nucleus is to lead to the secretion of high amounts of melatonin. Since high levels of melatonin secretion occur only at night, the elegant and simple solution to this woman's winter depression was to expose her to artificial sunlight in the form of fluorescent grow lights commonly used to grow plants.

Chapter 6 in the textbook, "Rhythms of the Brain," considers the role of circadian rhythms in humans and other animals. Rhythms of the body are ultimately tied to planetary cycles of day/night rhythms and seasonal light and temperature changes, and have a profound effect on human and animal function. Some bodily rhythms, such as sleep and wakefulness, occur on a daily basis, whereas other rhythms, such as the incidence of dreaming, occur many times during a day. The former are termed circadian rhythms, whereas the latter are termed ultradian rhythms. The third kind of rhythm, infradian rhythms, are found in such phenomena as seasonal migration and winter hibernation that occur less than once per day.

Pat Moore's difficulty was related to the lack of sufficient sunlight to suppress melatonin secretion. Other individuals experience depression due to a desynchronization of the circadian clocks. The surprising treatment for these patients involves "resetting" their biological clock by keeping them up all night, which effectively serves to resynchronize their biological rhythms. We are largely unaware of these rhythms, which when dysfunctional can produce severe symptoms. It also implies that we are all servants of the rhythms of the earth and thus share this bonding with all other life forms.

Environmental Isolation

What happens to biological rhythms when the ever-present cues of light, dark, temperature, and noise are removed? The answer to this question was provided by a remarkable French explorer, Michel Siffre, who spent six months in a deep cave, totally removed from all rhythmic environmental cues. When placed in such an environment an individual will not stay up constantly or sleep constantly but will develop a circadian rhythm generated from within the body and not as a result of environmental cues. In the case of the cave dweller, the average daily length turned out to be slightly less than 25 hours. This demonstrates rather conclusively that the body has a clock which is capable, by itself, of producing rhythmic changes in behavior. The definition of a internal rhythm is one that occurs without the presence of external stimuli.

Disrupted Rhythms

What happens if these internal bodily rhythms are disrupted? This most frequently occurs when we take extended airplane trips and cross several time zones. The phenomenon of jet lag is well known to travelers and is discussed at length in Chapter 6. Jet lag represents a desynchronization between the environmental cues of the new location and the bodily rhythms which still maintain their old periodicity. Seasoned travelers are aware of the effects of jet lag and try to arrange their schedules to minimize its impact. On occasion jet lag can lead to quite embarrassing situations, as was witnessed by President Reagan falling asleep during a papal address.

Many workers in the United States and throughout the world are regularly subjected to conditions guaranteed to interfere with their internal rhythms. Many "shift workers" rotate from working the daytime shift, to swing shift, to graveyard, and back to daytime--continuing this cycle throughout their working career. When asked, many of these workers report that it is very difficult trying to work when the body is gearing down to go to sleep. Then upon arriving at home, they are expected to go to bed when their body rhythm is gearing up to be awake. Not too surprisingly, such drastic shifts in their internal clocks lead to a deterioration in work performance as well as personal well-being.

The kinds of problems that can result from such inattention to biological rhythms include disorders of the cardiovascular system, digestive system, mental depression, and various sleep disorders. As is documented in the program, an experiment conducted in Utah altered the pattern of shift workers' schedules to be more consistent with bodily rhythms and observed that not only were the workers happier but productivity increased as well. While some of the beneficial effects of altering the shift work patterns for these workers might be attributed simply to the fact that people were paying attention to their needs and complaints, much of it is undoubtedly due to an increased recognition of the role of internal rhythms of the body and their consequences.

Violence

It has commonly been said that ours is a violent society. Certainly the history of human activities tends to support the contention that humans are violent animals. Since all behavior is a result of brain functioning, we might ask "What are the brain centers involved in violence and aggression"? Animal experimentation has sought to provide an answer to this question. A segment of this program shows a dramatic example of the ability to control aggression by manipulating brain circuitry. Dr. Jose Delgado implanted electrodes deep into the brain of a bull. When the electrodes were activated by radio control during a bull fight, the charging bull immediately broke off his attack. Similarly, electrodes placed into the brain of a domestic cat can produce either a rage attack or the stalking prey attach common to predatory animals. In the program we witness the tragic story of Mark, who was arrested for assaulting a young child. Upon medical examination it was discovered that his aggression behavior was due to the presence of a growing tumor near the hypothalamus. The pressure produced by this invading tumor resulted in aggressive behavior that was beyond his ability to control, behavior much like a raging animal. Upon removal of the cyst from Mark's brain, he completely recovered. This demonstrates rather dramatically how the more primitive aspects of subcortical brain activity can intrude on human behavior to produce unwanted results.

Sexual Behavior

The last segment of the program examines a topic of interest to most-- sexual behavior. In many animals sexual behavior is under the near exclusive control of neuroendocrine activity. Many females display periodic estrus cycles in which they come into heat, accepting the advances of an amorous male. Humans, on the other hand, are also influenced by social and cultural factors. Hormonal influences and social/cultural factors both play an important part in human sexual behavior. In the last segment of the program, we are introduced to Mitch, who has lost interest in sexual activity. As can be imagined such loss of libido can produce potentially serious problems between a husband and a wife. Mitch, of course, did not understand this curious lack of interest in sexual behavior and as a result was quite disturbed by what was happening to him. As is discussed by Dr. William Crowley, Mitch's problem involved the neuroendocrine system. Normally the hypothalamus releases a hormone called gonadatropin-releasing hormone which results in the release of gonadatropic hormones by the pituitary gland. These hormones influence the testes of the male and the ovaries of the female to release the gonadal hormones androgen and estrogen respectively. Mitch's difficulty related to an inability of his hypothalamus to release gonadatropin-releasing hormone. The solution to Mitch's problem was to provide him with a device to automatically and periodically inject into his body he missing gonadatropin-releasing hormone. This "portable hypothalamus" brought about the complete restoration of Mitch's sexual function through artificial means.

In this program we highlight a number of the biological rhythms and drives that are important in regulating human behavior. Many of these biological rhythms are occurring on a regular basis in each of us, yet are usually outside of our sphere of attention. As is shown dramatically in the sequences, such biological rhythms, in large part determined by subcortical structures, influence our lives in important and pervasive ways.

Textbook Chapter 6 expands upon the theme of this program to provide additional information about rhythmic behavior and its biological basis. Chapter 5 is concerned with homeostasis and examines the functions of the autonomic nervous system and the endocrine system, both topics related to the theme of this program.

PROGRAM 4: STRESS AND EMOTION

Introduction

In a museum at Harvard University rests the skull of Mr. Phineas Gage and a dynamite tamping iron that was blown through his head. As is dramatically recreated in the program, the tamping iron, in traveling through Phineas Gage's head, destroyed his frontal lobe. The result of this grievous wound was that Gage went from being a responsible, dedicated citizen to an emotional, unstable unfortunate. While lucky to have survived the accident, Phineas Gage went down in the annals of medical history as one of the classical cases demonstrating the effects of damage to the frontal lobes. The frontal lobes are generally thought to be one of the principal sites in the brain where judgment and emotional integration take place. The frontal lobes are richly connected with the limbic system which, deprived of the frontal lobe activity, produced the unstable emotional outbursts that were characteristic of Gage.

Stress

Today injuries from dynamite tamping irons are rare but there are many equally serious manifestations of effects on the brain resulting from modern society. As is documented in the program, one of the most severe problems facing humans today is chronic stress. Stress, in and of itself, is not necessarily a condition to be avoided. When an organism is placed in a stressful situation, there are physiologic changes that are designed to prepare the animal to "fight or flee." Heart rate is accelerated, norepinephrine is released to mobilize the sympathetic division of the autonomic nervous system, and other physiological variables are altered. The difficulty with stress in modern society is that we are rarely placed in a position where we can fight or flee. As it is so aptly stated in the program, "we can't fight the boss or flee the job." The result is that many individuals find themselves under chronic stress.

The problems produced by chronic stress are illustrated in air traffic controllers. One of the more stressful jobs that humans engage in, air traffic controllers are responsible for the safety of airliners flying the world's skyways. Controllers suffer from chronic stress and exhibit a high incidence of gastrointestinal problems, heart disease, and cancer.

What is it about a stressful situation that produces these effects? In experiments with laboratory animals, it has been shown that a stressful situation can be coped with as long as the animal is in control of the situation and can predict what is about to happen. In situations where the animal has no control and is unable to predict what is about to happen, the symptoms of chronic stress appear. For example, a rat placed in a jar of water from which it has previously escaped, will swim actively--searching for a way out. If, on the other hand, the animal learns that it cannot escape, it finds itself in a hopeless situation--it will then swim less actively and show symptoms of chronic stress.

General Adaptation Syndrome

The neurobiology of chronic stress is related to the physiological changes that occur to a stressful situation. With prolonged exposure to a stressor, the norepinephrine released by neurons in the locus coeruleus becomes depleted. The brain, however, contains mechanisms to guard against excess stress. The neurotransmitter, GABA, is an inhibitory neurotransmitter which acts to lower the excitability of the cells upon which it synapses. The first stage of defense against chronic stress is the activation of GABA synapses. However, with the continued application of a stressful stimulus, the GABA inhibitory circuitries will fail. The textbook (Chapter 7) describes the general adaptation syndrome that has been studied in great detail by Hans Selye. In the general adaptation syndrome we see that organisms go through three stages of response to stressful situations. The first stage involves an _alarm reaction_, which arouses the sympathetic nervous system to cope with the stressor. The second phase in the stress reaction involves _resistance_, where the body mobilizes its resources to overcome the stress producing event. In most diseases and injuries, antibodies rush to the site. In psychological stress, however, the sympathetic nervous system prepares one to fight or flee. If the stressor continues, the third phase of the stress reaction sets in-- _exhaustion_. The effects of chronic stress in modern society can lead to the third stage of the stress response. Drugs have been developed to help humans deal with chronic stress. The drug Valium (a benzodiazepine) is the most commonly used anti-stress drug which acts by improving the inhibitory action of GABA. The effectiveness of benzodiazepines suggests that these drugs are acting on endogenous benzodiazepine receptors. The naturally occurring neurotransmitter or neuromodulator that act upon these receptors has yet to be discovered, but the search for the brain's own anti-stress chemical continues.

Panic

A segment of this program deals with individuals suffering from "panic attacks." These attacks of spontaneous terror "I'm going to die" seem to involve a massive autonomic nervous system activation triggered by some environmental event. People suffering from panic attacks are often on guard for the next attack and will attempt to avoid situations (crowds, subways) that trigger the panic attack. The treatment for such individuals involves teaching them the relaxation response, which may involve biofeedback conditioning to promote relaxation in the presence of the stressful situation.

In the last segment of this program we see the dramatic results of chemical manipulation of the brain, the utilization of a local anesthetic given during childbirth. We witness a Caesarean birth, wherein the mother is locally anesthetized with a spinal anesthetic during the entire surgical procedure.

In this program we highlight the role of stress on emotional responses and the physiologic effects that accompany prolonged stressful situations. Chapter 7 considers the various theories of emotionality that have developed historically and relates them to current thought regarding the brain structures that mediate emotion. We trace the role of the limbic system in the development of emotionality and discover the scientific approaches to the study of emotions that have been developed in the last several decades. As is discussed in relation to childbirth, the role of the nervous system in the perception of pain is one that has achieved considerable advances in the past ten years. We now know that the brain employs its own pain-killing chemical, neuromodulators known as endorphins.

PROGRAM 5: LEARNING AND MEMORY

In this program we examine one of the frontiers of the neurosciences-- brain processes that occur during learning and memory. Learning and memory are such ubiquitous processes that we are generally aware of them only when they fail to occur. Imagine life without learning and memory: existing entirely in the here and the now without access to previous experiences and without awareness of the past. Such cases of total amnesia wiping out all traces of the past are extremely rare; what is more common is a memory defect wherein certain memories are preserved, perhaps from much earlier in life, leaving later memories completely obliterated.

Memory may be one of the most mysterious of the brain's activities. Many questions remain to be answered before we can claim to understand the brain processes underlying these phenomena. What is memory and learning? Where does it occur in the brain? How does it work? These basic questions are at present still unanswered, although many scientists believe we are getting close to understanding.

As is shown in the opening scenes of this program, the establishing of memories early in life is a fundamental operation which serves to put into perspective all future behavior and experience. It may come as a surprise then to reflect on the fact that few memories are retained from early childhood. As Dr. Donald Hebb states in the program, few memories are present before five years of age (the exceptions are almost invariably traumatic events). While we don't know the reason for this lack of memory encoding during the formative years, it is possible that the brain is sufficiently engaged in other processes, such as developing its basic structure and laying down sensory and motor patterns, that memories for experiential events are put on hold until later in life.

You will see in this program that brain scientists employ one of two strategies in their study of memory and learning. They may employ a "bottom-up" strategy, going from molecular to the molar level of analysis. In this approach they seek to understand the operation of nerve cells and circuits that might underlie memory, eventually to apply it to whole organisms. The alternative approach, the "top-down" approach, works in the reverse direction, beginning with the observable facts of memory and trying to decipher the underlying cellular mechanisms. In this program we will see examples of both approaches.

The history of investigation into the brain substrates of learning and memory have been faced with a long-standing paradox. The question that triggered the paradox is a very simple one: is there a brain location for memories? Dr. Donald Hebb, now a retired neuroscientist, worked with two of the pioneers in this field, Drs. Wilder Penfield and Karl Lashley. Both these scientists were interested in the brain substrates of memory, Penfield utilized a top-down approach, whereas Lashley used a bottom-up approach. Penfield, working with

167

human neurosurgical patients, utilized electrical stimulation of the brain to elicit memories from the locally anesthetized patient. He observed that particular memories could be triggered by electrical stimulation of the temporal lobe. Lashley, working with rats in behavioral experiments, concluded that memories were not localized to any specific region of the cortex or elsewhere. Lashley, placed lesions in the rat's cortex in an attempt to determine which areas were encoding the memory of the event. He was unable to produce specific lesions that eliminated memories for the behavioral task; rather the size of the lesion correlated well with the amount of the defect in memory.

Thus we have the paradox that one set of observations suggests memory is located in a particular place, wherein another set of observations suggests that it does not. Contemporary scientists believe that this paradox is more apparent than real. It is currently thought that the storage of memory seems to be located wherever processing occurs. Since we know that processing occurs in widespread brain areas, it follows that many areas of the brain may be involved in memory storage. Penfield was able to activate specific memories in his patients by electrically stimulating one component of the distributed memory trace.

Memory disorders can be quite devastating to an individual. In the program, we see Peter, a man who appears quite normal except for his memory disorder. Peter suffered from a brain infection which resulted in amnesia. Peter is unable to remember very much about events that have occurred since his brain infection. Since his memory for older events is normal, this gives us a clue as to brain processes involved in memory. It suggests that whatever brain circuits are involved in Peter's condition, they are not necessary in extracting older memories from storage. Apparently, Peter has lost the ability to lay down new memories, not retrieve old ones.

The hippocampus of Peter's brain has been damaged by the brain infection. Numerous observations have shown that the hippocampus is involved in memory operations in the human brain. The textbook (Chapter 8) describes the effect of lesions to the hippocampus on several patients. These patients, like Peter, are unable to encode new memories yet can successfully retrieve older ones.

The work of Dr. Gary Lynch, as shown in the program, provides evidence from animal experiments that there are changes occuring in the hippocampus during the formation of physiological changes that may underlie learning. The synaptic structure and number of synaptic connections in the hippocampus change as the result of these physiological changes. Thus we see that it is possible that the laying down of memories in the brain involves subtle changes in the way neurons communicate with one another. The implication of this is that learning results in an actual change in brain organization. As you are going through this course, it can be safely assumed that there are physical and chemical changes that are occurring in your brain which may last for your lifetime.

The work of Professor Changeaux of Paris suggests the surprising result that learning involves an elimination of neural connections. While in some sense the opposite to the results of Dr. Lynch, these observations of neuronal death and synapse elimination have been substantiated in the developing nervous system. During development considerably more neurons and synapses are formed than are needed for proper functioning later in life. One of the things happening during the development of the nervous system is the selective elimination or death of these apparently unnecessary brain elements. While this may be contrary to our usual way of thinking about learning, wherein we assume that something is being added, we must remain open the possibility that something existing is being removed. Dr. Changeaux's observations also suggest that learning begins in the womb. Relating back to our earlier discussion regarding why memories are not encoded in infancy, one may again suggest that the nervous system must learn all sorts of things about its internal and external environment including such processes as learning to coordinate the muscles, sensory organs and the like. None of these phenomena are consciously referred to later in life, but are absolutely essential for the proper operation of the body.

The program documents some forms of "memory magic" that to the average individual seem quite remarkable indeed. Shown is a man who, through what may appear to many to be a bizarre train of association, is capable of remembering long lists of random numbers. The strategy that this memory magician employs to aid in the storage of these numbers is to associate them with physical objects and places. This is a commonly employed tactic for those individuals who must remember many details in the course of their daily activities.

Later in the show we meet still another individual with memory disturbances. Ken suffered from a brain infection which damaged his hippocampus and other structures resulting in a condition where he, like Peter, cannot form new memories. This segment of the program dramatically demonstrates the ubiquity of memory functioning in every day activities and points out the devastating nature of memory disturbances. Ken is a man trapped in the past and immediate present. Imagine not knowing what you had done in the last hour, day or month. You would find life considerably changed as a result.

We see another individual suffering from encephalitis - a young girl named Laurie. Laurie, unlike the other two patients, completely lost all of her memories and now must relearn her own past experiences and background.

In Dr. Donald Hebb we see a renowned scientist who is watching his own brain grow old and gradually lose some of the capabilities it once had. In Dr. Hebb we are observing the effects of the normal aging process. For some individuals afflicted with Alzheimer's disease, this process is tremendously accelerated in an abnormal loss of all intellectual functions. As we shall see in more detail in Program 8 and in the text (Chapter 10), Alzheimer's disease results from the unexplained death of neurons in the nucleus basalis. While there are some potential treatments for conditions like Alzheimer's disease, the patient afflicted with a senile dementia faces an uncertain and progressively deteriorating future.

There are many questions remaining regarding the brain's functioning in learning and memory. We are only now beginning to see avenues that may promise to shed light on these currently mysterious brain phenomena. In the text (Chapter 8) you will read that in experimental animals there are a number of neural changes associated with learning and memory which may provide the answers to these questions. You will read that, in addition to the hippocampus which has been implicated in certain forms of memory, other brain regions, such as the cerebellum, are certainly involved as well.

In this program we deal primarily with long-term memory. There are two other forms of memory that may involve different brain substrates: immediate recall and short-term memory. Since learning and memory involve synaptic interactions between neurons, the student may not be surprised to learn that studies have shown that drugs which can manipulate neurotransmitters, are effective in altering learning and memory functions. As is consistent with the idea that physical changes occur in the brain following learning, there is evidence that protein synthesis, a necessary ingredient in creating new neuronal elements, appears to be involved as well. You will learn about procedural and declarative memory. The distinction between these two foundational forms of memory may underlie the ability of the memory magician to employ procedural memory strategies in encoding declarative memory events, such as strings of numbers.

PROGRAM 6: THE TWO BRAINS

In this program we focus on the "seat of intelligence", the cortex. A remarkable tissue capable of providing humans with the ultimate in artistic, scientific and intellectual functioning, the cortex represents a frontier area of the brain sciences.

A major theme of this program is the specialization of the cortex. Not too many years ago it was thought that most of the areas of the cortex, particularly the association cortex, were not specialized and functioned as a sort of computer for the higher operations of the brain. The more we learn about the cortex, however, the more we appreciate that it contains numerous specializations which, in the words of Dr. Norman Geschwind, serve us well because they increase the intellectual capabilities of the brain.

When viewing the gross brain, one of the most obvious anatomical features is the existence of two symmetrical halves, or hemispheres. The cortical hemispheres are normally connected by a massive fiber bundle known as the corpus callosum. In a small number of severely epileptic patients, the corpus callosum has been surgically severed in order to prevent the spread of epilepsy. One of the split brain patients, Vicki, is featured in the program doing a variety of common, everyday activities. Watch her closely and see if you can detect any differences in her behavior from that of a normal individual. Probably you cannot. However, when subject to rigorous testing which presents visual material to either her left or right hemisphere, remarkable differences are immediately apparent. In one scene, we see one-half of Vicki's brain remarkably unaware of the activities of the other half. The conclusion is rather compelling - she, as a result of this rare surgery, possesses two consciousness's inside of one head.

Neuroscientists have known long before the advent of split-brain operations that language functions in the brain were not equally re-presented on the two hemispheres. From the early work of Professors Broca and Wiernicke, we know that the language cortex is found in the dominant hemisphere of the brain. For most individuals the left hemis-phere is dominant. This knowledge was obtained from studying patients suffering from strokes. In the program, Mr. Charles Landry displays the effects of a stroke that affected regions of his language cortex. Still able to think and understand much language, the effect of the stroke on his ability to produce language is most devastating and, unfortunately may be permanent.

The non-dominant hemisphere of the brain is specialized as well. The program documents the importance of spatial information in the daily activities of all of us. It is this type of spatial analysis that is within the province of the non-dominant hemisphere, usually the right hemisphere.

The Japanese language is unique in that it contains two forms of writing, Kana, a phonetic form that is thought to primarily engage the dominant hemisphere, and Kanji, an ideogram or pictorial form which is primarily processed in the non-dominant hemisphere. Japanese stroke victims display different symptoms on these two forms depending upon the location of the stroke. Importantly, the distribution of language activities in the Japanese brain is a result of cultural influences interacting with genetic specializations. It used to be thought that the wiring of the brain was entirely genetically determined and that all functions were wired in by heredity. The demonstration of brain processing differences among the Japanese clearly indicates that cultural and environmental influences can have a profound effect on the functioning of the human brain. The idea that culture can mold brain is an old one. It has been confirmed in the case of Japanese language.

A segment of the program focuses on still another aspect of cultural influence on brain organization. This time taking us to Australia and joining a tribe of Aboriginal children. While failing to do as well on verbal tests as do white Australian children, the Aborigines do much better on tests of their spatial memory. This is thought to be because the Aborigine children are raised in a natural environment wherein spatial information of the world around them attains a significance that is lacking in the case of the white Australian children raised in cities. When faced with a problem to be solved, the white and Aborigine children used different strategies to solve it, strategies based upon their own cultural experiences and reflected in brain organization and function.

A main thesis of this course is that all behavior is ultimately explainable in terms of the actions of neurons and of neuron circuits. Clearly, males and females behave differently....do they possess different brains? While we cannot answer this question definitively, we do know that males and females differ in terms of the incidence of left-handedness and in terms of the incidence of some forms of mental dysfunction including dyslexia. That these differences are the result of cellular processes is emphasized by Professor Geshwind who believes that the gonadal hormone, testosterone, is responsible for sex differences in the brain as well as handedness differences. The power of gonadal hormones to alter behavior and function is shown in the case of an unfortunate women by the name of Mrs. Smith, who, although genetically male has a female body and lifestyle. Mrs. Smith's body did not respond to circulating testosterone when she was an infant and as a result of her body developed in feminine form although her genetic sex and brain sex remain male.

The role of testosterone in brain differentiation is also examined in a segment with Professor Dorner of East Germany. Professor Dorner addresses the controversial question of the biological basis of male homosexuality. His conclusion is that the role of testosterone is intimately involved in determining the sexual differentiation of the brain and thus, the sexual behavioral preferences shown by an individual.

It is, of course, difficult to separate the role of experience in shaping sex-related behavior. For example, most adults behave in a stereotyped manner toward male or female infants. Boys are urged to be active and to explore their environment, whereas girls are encouraged to be quieter and are spoken to more. The toys that are given to these infants are different: girls get dolls, boys get hammers and baseball bats. In a fascinating segment of the program, infant boys are dressed as girls to see how adults behave toward them.

172

In the normal, integrated human brain all of these functions and more are put back together. We do not see the world only with our left hemisphere or only with our right hemisphere. We do not analyze language solely with Wernicke's and Broca's areas; rather all regions of the brain contribute their special expertise to the solution of the problem of life.

In the textbook (Chapter 9) we explore other aspects of cortical function. One feature of the human brain that may be unique is consciousness. We define what is meant by consciousness and look at the development of consciousness and its brain underpinnings. We explore further the specializations of the cortex in language and other functions and examine the bizarre condition of "multiple personality," a topic also presented in Program 8.

PROGRAM 7: MADNESS

Bizarre thought forms, strange associations, paranoia, inappropriate affect . . . MADNESS! Probably the worst afflication known to mankind, mental illness can take a devastating toll on the victim and the victim's family and friends. In this program we investigate mental illness and in particular, one of the most severe forms of mental illness, schizophrenia. For those who have known family or friends to be afflicted with a psychotic disease, the full spectrum of the disease needs no telling. A total disorder of the whole person, wherein thought, movement, and perception, are all altered in sometimes unpredictable ways, mental illness takes a terrible toll. This program shows to those who have not experienced it directly, the personal trauma of the afflicted and the heart-wrenching effects on family and friends.

Gerry, an ex-policeman, suffers from schizophrenia. As you watch Gerry talk with his therapist and his parents, pay attention not only to his speech and the content of his speech, but notice the aimless, purposeless behaviors that he displays. Notice, too, the behavior of the therapist: calm, nondirective, seeking more information. As is represented in Gerry, schizophrenia is a disorder of the highest, most human functions of the brain. Typically, the schizophrenic withdraws from loved ones just when the patient is going through a terrible personal experience and could benefit most from friendship and love.

The severely sick schizophrenic requires hospitalization. Even as humane as today's treatment facilities are, they still represent awful scenes of patients experiencing agony. While drug therapy has made a remarkable difference in the treatment of the schizophrenic, schizophrenia remains a horrible disease with a poor prognosis and a long-term course. One-third of the patients will get better, one-third will be in and out of mental hospitals for the rest of their lives, and one-third will become chronic schizophrenics requiring constant hospitalization.

The neurosciences are beginning learn something of the brain substrates underlying schizophrenia. We know that drugs that are effective in blocking the neurotransmitter dopamine are useful in relieving some of the symptoms of schizophrenia. We know too, as is shown in this program, that there is a sizable genetic component to schizophrenia. This knowledge removes the great burden of guilt often experienced by a family who think themselves responsible for creating a bad environment responsible for the disease. However, this knowledge poses another dilemma, that of the parent who is confronted with the existence of schizophrenia in his or her family background and the debate as to whether to have children who might then become afflicted.

Gerry's mother, in a filmed interview, equates what she sees in her son with a "living hell." This can be readily appreciated when viewing the interaction between Gerry and his mother and father. The parents display remarkable tolerance for Gerry's inappropriate outbursts and bizarre train of thought.

Sigmund Freud maintained that the psychoses like schizophrenia were the result of a bad childhood (he also admitted that schizophrenia is not treatable with psychoanalysis.) Whereas it is possible that there may be triggers in the environment that serve to set off a schizophrenic episode, it seems likely that a hereditary factor results in predisposition toward the disease, which, when given the appropriate environmental trigger, results in the development of mental illness.

Imagine what it must be like for a parent to watch their child become schizophrenic. As is stated in a segment of the program, "You adopt a stranger" when the disease occupies their mind. The parents' frustration and lack of an appropriate response to a schizophrenic child is clearly shown in this program.

The program emphasizes the tremendous impact of schizophrenic processes on the patient and the patient's family. It suggests that research into the cellular and genetic basis of schizophrenia may eventually lead to a cure. The textbook (Chapter 10) expands upon these themes in considerable detail and exposes the student to other forms of brain dysfunction, principally the degenerative and affective disorders (which are not dealt with in this program).

PROGRAM 8: STATES OF MIND

In this program we focus on more integrative aspects of higher brain functioning. We examine dreaming, creativity, attention, and such abnormalities of brain as multiple personalities, uncontrolled aggression, and Alzheimer's dementia.

We have all experienced the mystery of the dream--the bizarre, the unexpected, the illogical nature of dreaming. While we do not understand the necessity for dreaming, we are beginning to know more about the biological basis of dreams. The brain circuitry and neuro-transmitters involved in dreams are beginning to be known, however, the underlying fundamental mystery of "why dream?" still remains elusive. As Dr. Alan Hobson see it, "during dreams we see the creative process unleashed." Although the everyday dreamer may not appreciate such a statement, dreams have been known to provide the answers to problems. The chemical ring structure of benzene, for example, became clear in a symbolic dream. And if by creativity we mean simply the ability to construct new and novel experiences, then certainly dreams qualify as a creative endeavor.

Creativity is an area barely touched by the neurosciences. Yet it is a fundamental activity of advanced brains. Human endeavors are marked by continued creativity. The entire social and economic advancement of cultures depends upon continued creativity. Not limited to human brains, creativity, as is documented in the program, can be observed in wild animals as well. We see the intriguing obser-vation of a monkey discovering how to separate corn from the sand upon which it is found. The discovery that by throwing the corn and sand mixture into wat the corn will float and the sand sink was a fundamental creative insight which was then passed on to the offspring of the monkey as well as to other monkeys. While we don't understand the brain processes underlying creativity, we do know something of the dynamics of the process. For example, it is known that creativity is a skill that can be developed. By engaging in "creative activities" one can learn how to approach problems in creative ways. This, of course, is one of the objectives of education. Perhaps one of the solutions to the practical application of creativity is in the ability to focus one's attention onto various aspects of the surroundings. The ability to focus attention is essential to bringing the cognitive abilities of an individual to bear on a problem.

A segment of this program focuses on Tony, an individual posses-sing fifty independent personalities. Initially thought by some to be a hoax, we now know that multiple personality is an affliction which, while quite rare, must be recognized as a disease entity and therefore, following the theme of this course, one ultimately explainable by brain processes. All of us have multiple personalities. We are different persons to our grandmother, our peers, and our sweetheart. However, a normal individual always remains in control. We know that we are simply modifying our behavior to fit the circumstances. The individual suffering from multiple personalities does not have the ability to remain in control and, instead, the personalities control the individual. In some cases it is very difficult to know who really represents the individual. There may be battles between the personalities, as is documented in the program. The personalities contained within such an individual appear and decline, just as individuals are born and die. We now know that brain function and the distribution of brain activity is different with each personality, supporting the belief that there is a biologic base to this disease.

Another facet of creativity is shown in an artist suffering from damage to his parietal lobe. He experiences a phenomenon known as "neglect." The left side of his face ceases to exist for this artist. He is not blind--his vision is perfectly normal, rather he fails to attend to things on the left side of the visual world. Other patients suffering from neglect do such bizarre things as fail to dress one-half of their body, or apply make-up to only one-half of the face. In the program we see that the artist perceives the neglected (left) side of his face much differently than the right side.

All would agree that the rising incidence of drug abuse is a tragedy of acute proportions. The widespread use of narcotics and hallucinogenic drugs creates tremendous personal and societal havoc. Yet, when confronted with a drug like "angel dust" (PCP), a hallucinogen, the neuroscientist appreciates that its action on the brain implies that it is interacting with chemical receptors on nerve cells. As strange as it may seem that the brain would naturally employ a chemical having the effects of angel dust, the conclusion must be that some aspect of the nervous system utilizes a chemical very similar to PCP in its normal operation. An individual under the influence of angel dust can often exhibit violent, uncontrolled aggression. Perhaps it is the function of the naturally occurring chemical to regulate aggressive behavior among all of us. Certainly aggression has played an important role in the history of mankind and perhaps this is a clue to the brain substrates of aggression. If so, one hopes for the day when man's aggressive nature may be brought under control, perhaps through the application of fundamental advances in our understanding of the brain chemistry of aggression.

We all hate to grow old. The thought of becoming infirm and forgetful, perhaps compounded with physical illness, is something that no one looks forward to. However these problems are insignificant compared with the future promised to the Alzheimer's patient. Common among the aged, Alzheimer's disease is a deterioration of the higher mental functions of the human brain. A progressive disease for which no cure is known and no treatment currently exists, Alzheimer's disease involves memory loss, a declining intellectual capability, and a destruction of the highest, most human functions of the brain. As the patient in the program pleads, "I wish I could hold back time." While no treatment is known today, a recent discovery has shown that the disease seems to be related to a degeneration of cells in the nucleus basalis, neurons containing acetylcholine that have widespread projection to the cortex and other brain areas. While we do not have a treatment for Alzheimer's disease today, the emerging knowledge of the biological basis of this disease may offer a potential cure in the years to come. It might prove possible to transplant into the region of the nucleus basalis other tissues capable of secreting acetylcholine, the neurotransmitter which is being depleted by the disease process.

Not all research into brain function is done by biologists working on nervous tissue. Some prefer to create computer equivalents of brain circuits and processes in order to test theoretical ideas about brain functioning. Both neurons and computer chips hare certain properties that may make such an enterprise valuable. Those individuals working in this field which is termed "artificial intelligence" utilize the power of modern computers to simulate the activities of brain cells in neural circuits. From this analysis new insights may arise as to the functioning of the biological brain. Critics of artificial intelligence research point out that it is better to study the biological brain rather than to make computer models based on how we think the biological brain might work. One such answer to these critics is that all forms of intellectual endeavor are potentially valuable and one cannot foresee where breakthroughs will come from.

In this, the final program, we see that brain and mind are intimately interwoven such that it is impossible to have mind without the physical substrate of brain. The more we learn about the structure and function of the brain, the more we will, in turn learn about the operation of the mind. As you reflect on the content of these eight programs and the textbook chapters that go along with them, it is hoped that you have gained an added appreciation for the intricacies and capabilities of the brain. Truly representing a frontier of modern scientific effort, the neurosciences strive to understand the functioning human brain in ways that may have pronounced impact on the future of humankind.